# BEAUTY THERAPIST'S
# GUIDE TO
# PROFESSIONAL
# PRACTICE AND
# CLIENT CARE

## ANDREA BARHAM

LONGMAN

**Pearson Education Limited**
Edinburgh Gate
Harlow
Essex CM20 2JE
England

and Associated Companies around the world

*Visit us on the World Wide Web at:*
www.pearsoned-ema.com

First published 1999

© Pearson Education Limited 1999

ISBN 0 582 32661-3

*British Library Cataloguing-in-Publication Data*
A catalogue record for this book is available from the British Library.

Typeset by 32
Printed in Singapore (COS)

# Contents

## CHAPTER FOUR  *Look After Yourself* — *33*

## CHAPTER FIVE  *Make your Salon Inviting* — *43*

## CHAPTER SIX  *Look Professional* — *50*

## CHAPTER SEVEN  *Act Professionally* — *58*

*To my husband Andy, for – everything.*

# Acknowledgements

I would like to thank the following people for their invaluable help in compiling this book: Andrew Barham for his salon photography; Tracy Nicholls and the staff of Images Beauty Rooms, Ramsden Heath and Amber Yates and the staff of Spa Esprit, Billericay for modelling for the photographs; Ellisons for providing photographs of equipment; Salon System for providing photos of products; Jane Strubel for reviewing advice on retailing; Dawn Cragg for advice on micropigmentation and the beauty therapy students of Thurrock Technical College for critiquing the manuscript prior to publication.

# What this book is about

*This book will show you how and why to be professional.*

## What's in this book

You are reading this book. That shows that you care about being professional in your work. The best time to think about ethics and professionalism is at the beginning of your career, during your training.

Knowing how to be professional benefits you just as much as your clients. As your professionalism grows, so will your confidence. Good standards will serve you well throughout your working life. Read this book alongside your beauty therapy textbooks. It's about how to look after your clients, your colleagues, your salon and not least, yourself.

Begin with Part One: *Professionalism in the Salon*, which relates to NVQ1 and 2. Part Two: *Professionalism with Clients* relates to NVQ2, 3 and 4 but read it as you like – some points may be useful later in your career but all knowledge provides a good background to help you strive for excellence throughout your career.

Words that appear in bold type are defined in the Glossary at the back of the book. You may like to discuss the questions in *What do you think?* at the end of some chapters with your tutors, colleagues or fellow students.

## What isn't in this book

This book does not detail practical or theoretical beauty therapy treatment application.

## What are ethics?

Ethics are 'moral principles'. Having ethics means knowing the right way to act and always acting that way. This book will give examples of ethical behaviour to help you decide for yourself what ethics mean to you.

## What is professionalism?

Once you qualify and charge for your services you will be a 'professional' rather than a 'trainee' or 'amateur'. You will be expected to act 'professionally', that is, to have the highest standards and be businesslike.

# PART ONE

# Professionalism in the Salon

# Chapter One

# *Your Chosen Profession*

*Beauty treatment is not a matter of life and death … to some clients, it's much more important than that.*

## Why do clients visit beauty salons?

To many clients, beauty salons offer much more than beauty treatment; they represent a haven from the outside world, a longed-for lifestyle or dreamed-of image. In today's automated, self-service world, beauty therapy is a personal service that no machine can replace.

What is the aim of the beauty therapist? Broadly, to do no harm, and try to do some good. There is much good to be done in beauty therapy and much satisfaction to be gained for both therapist and client.

## Who makes a good therapist?

As a beauty therapist, you will need to:

- be fit and healthy – massage, for example, is strenuous
- be caring
- be enthusiastic
- be able to put people at their ease
- have an interest in how the body works
- enjoy working hard
- have good manual dexterity for electrolysis and make-up application
- enjoy working with women
- have tact, sympathy and patience.

Some artistic ability is useful for applying colour cosmetics.

**Figure 1.1**
Excel in client care

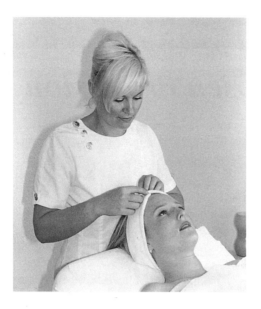

# Vocational training

Having a vocation means having a strong feeling for wanting to follow a certain profession. You will spend many years in your chosen profession. For a successful career, you need sound training. As a student or apprentice, you will gain all the skills, expertise and experience you need to reach a professional standard. You will not have to take on too much responsibility too soon. Students who complete a modern apprenticeship or college diploma course show they are serious about their career and willing to invest time and effort in it.

## What is good about vocational training?

*You* are the active ingredient in a vocational profession. There is plenty of scope for you to get out of it what you want. The big plus in a **service industry** such as beauty therapy is that you get instant responses from your clients. The better your service, the bigger your **clientele** – and maybe the higher your income. In other words, the more you put in, the more you get out.

With enthusiasm and dedication, any student who excels at client care and practical treatment can go on to manage or own a highly successful salon.

## Make the most of your training

Everyone starts out not knowing about their chosen profession. But how do we learn? There are two ways:

- Someone tells us – maybe a tutor or book.
- We find out for ourselves.

> **Remember:** You only get one training. Take this opportunity to find out and learn as much as you can from your tutors, colleagues and clients.

During training, be sure to take advantage of the opportunity to practise every treatment thoroughly on models. Now is the time to concentrate on those treatments you feel least confident about.

- Make the most of quiet times in the salon. Offer to perform treatments on your colleagues, then ask them for suggestions on how you can improve your practical skills.
- Ask if you can watch your colleagues perform treatments on clients. (Your colleague will need to choose a client who won't mind.)
- Ask qualified and unqualified colleagues to perform the occasional treatment on you. Notice different pressures, speeds, techniques and the overall sensation. You can sometimes learn more from a bad treatment than a good one.

> **Remember:** Even after you are fully qualified, keep learning from your colleagues and clients throughout your working life. The mark of a true professional is never to stop learning.

## Why is so much background knowledge needed?

What's the point of learning so much theory in a practical profession? Most people can learn to copy a procedure, but if you don't learn the accompanying theory, you will have nothing to back up your skill with. Without knowing the theory, how will you:

- understand new products, methods of treatment and scientific advances in the beauty world?
- judge what is sound theory and what is advertising blurb and sales patter? Some treatments and equipment are more profitable for sales companies than beneficial for clients.
- answer your clients simple-sounding questions such as: 'Why don't pressure points tan on the sunbed?'
- give clients sound advice?

> **Remember:** Students who lack the back-up of theory only have half the story. They will always be at a professional disadvantage.

### Develop a taste for background reading

You need to know all the information in your practical textbooks. Read them without your tutor prompting you. Read the beauty therapy trade magazines in your college or salon. These trade magazines are available to borrow from a library in your county. There are two types, editorially led magazines and advertiser-led magazines.

- Editorially led magazines inform the therapist.
- Advertiser-led magazines are mostly concerned with promoting products for the beauty industry. For this reason, they are sometimes free.

You are fortunate if you have access to a specialized college library, but if not, you can still borrow the same books by joining your local library. A list of all the books currently in print is kept on your library's automated network. You can gain access to this through your library's public computer. (Ask a librarian if you're not sure how to use it.) For the price of a cup of coffee, you can request any book from the library computer and your library will get it for you to borrow for as long as you need. This way you can borrow any beauty therapy textbook and any beauty book intended for the public.

The more you read, the more you will notice that authors have different opinions. Sometimes you will have to use your own judgement and experience when deciding whose opinion is correct.

## *Tools and equipment*

When you begin training, you will need to buy beauty therapy tools. As a professional, always buy the best tools you can afford. Good-quality tools are easier to work with and will maintain your professional image.

As soon as you begin training, visit your local beauty wholesalers. There is no joining fee. Look in the *Yellow Pages* under *Hairdressing and Beauty Supplies* to find the nearest ones. As a trainee, you are entitled to shop there for equipment and products. (Saving money is useful for all trainees.)

> **Remember:** The wholesale prices *do not* include **VAT**. The current **VAT** percentage will be added to your bill at the cash desk.

Many salons find mail-order beauty suppliers more convenient. Find mail-order suppliers in trade magazines or at trade fairs. They sometimes have a 'minimum order' and charge for postage and packing.

## *About the beauty world*

These job titles are used in the beauty world:

- A **manicurist** is qualified to give beauty treatment to hands and feet.
- A **beautician** is qualified to treat mainly the face, hands and feet.
- A **beauty therapist** is qualified to treat the body including the use of electrical treatments such as **electro-epilation**.
- An **electrologist** is qualified in **electro-epilation**. This is a more accurate term for the treatment the public call **electrolysis**.
- **Aesthetician** is sometimes used as an alternative term for a beautician or beauty therapist. It comes from the word 'aesthetic' which means 'to do with beauty'.
- A **beauty consultant** has a short training, usually by a cosmetic company, to advise in-store on its own brand of make-up and skin care.
- A **dietician** or nutritionist is qualified to advise on diet, exercise and body shape.
- A make-up artist may or may not have a formal qualification. Make-up artists often freelance in the film, video and fashion industry and portrait photography.

# Getting a job

Competition for work in salons is always very fierce because more beauty therapists are trained than are needed. The more professional you are, the higher your chances are of being the successful applicant.

## How to get a Saturday or evening job in a salon

These jobs are very popular but you can 'get your foot in the door' early by arranging your own work experience. Ask your local salon if you can sit with the receptionist or salon junior for a couple of hours on Saturday or in the evening, for no pay, to gain salon experience. If you are helpful, you will be asked to stand in (for pay) when the current junior is on holiday, is sick or leaves.

## Application letter

When applying for a job, increase your chances of getting an interview by following traditional job application conventions:

- Write your application letter on plain white, unruled note paper in blue or black ink.
- If your letter begins with the person's name, close with 'Yours sincerely'.
- If your letter begins with 'Dear Sir or Madam', close with 'Yours faithfully' – but it's always best to find out the name of the owner or manager when you write.
- Print your name clearly below your signature.
- Provide a telephone number if you have one.
- Enclose a brief curriculum vitae.

## Curriculum vitae

Curriculum vitae (CV) means 'course of life' and is a brief list of your education, qualifications and previous jobs. Figure 1.2 is an example of a newly qualified student's CV.

- Type, print or neatly write your CV.
- Leave out headings where you have nothing to fill in. For example, don't include the heading 'Voluntary Experience' if you don't have any.
- Check with referees (people who will give you a reference) that it's okay to give their names before you do so.

## The interview

If you turn up … eventually … pondering the possibility that you may like to work in the salon for a while, you may as well have stayed in bed. Salon employers can afford to be very selective.

It's been estimated that employers make their minds up about job applicants within the first three minutes of meeting them. They spend the rest of the interview looking and listening for indications that their first impressions were right.

A positive attitude and image are just as important as paper qualifications. Your prospective employer will check your appearance to see if you know how a professional

**Figure 1.2**
A brief curriculum
vitae

20 Road Street, Anytown, County

Tel 01234 567890

Date of Birth 20 Month 19XX

Ann Other

| **Education** | From Date to Date | Anytown Infant School |
|---|---|---|
| | From Date to Date | Anytown Junior School |
| | From Date to Date | Anytown Senior School |
| | From Date to Date | Anytown Technical College |

**Qualifications and awards**

GCSE Human Biology, grade x, GCSE English language, grade x, GCSE Maths grade x

NVQ 1 and 2 in Beauty Therapy

Bronze Duke of Edinburgh Award

**Languages**  GCSE French, grade x

**Work experience**  From Date to Date  New You Beauty Salon, Anytown

**Volunteer experience**  Hospital visitor at St Anywhere's

**Summer jobs**  From Date to Date  Anytown Newsagents

**Previous employment**  Part-time manicurist at New You Beauty Salon

**Interests and hobbies**  Reading, art, swimming and modern dance

**References**  Mr J Bloggs, 30 Road Avenue, Anytown, County, Teacher.

Mrs P Person, 20 Road Street, Anytown, County, Civil Servant.

**Extracurricular activities**  Member of Anytown Dance Club

**Community activities**  Help at Anytown After-School Club

**Professional memberships**  Student member of BABTAC

beauty therapist should look. If you fail the visual test, you won't get a chance to impress with your practical skills or qualifications.

An employer will expect you to arrive ten minutes early, smartly dressed and discreetly made-up. She will judge how much you want the job by how much effort you put into getting ready for the interview. Remember to take your uniform with you for a practical demonstration.

## Work prospects

The more work skills you have, the better your chances of finding employment. Once experienced, therapists can work in a variety of settings including hotels, cruise liners, health farms, airliners and posts abroad. Many qualified therapists become self-employed, buy a franchise, start up a salon from scratch or buy a business already running.

Some therapists specialize in areas of beauty such as colour consultancy, **electro-epilation** or make-up artistry, but the vast majority work as all-round therapists. Due to budget constraints, paramedical posts are generally voluntary. As therapists move on, salon staff turnover can be high. It is quite possible to reach managerial level within two or three years of qualifying.

A beauty therapy qualification is a useful background to a career as a sales representative for a cosmetic or equipment company. Studying for a Certificate of Education (Cert Ed) will allow a qualified therapist to teach at a private beauty therapy training school or Further Education College.

> **Please note:** To simplify the text, I have referred to clients, therapists, tutors, owners and managers as 'she' throughout this book. However, it should be noted that there is a small but growing number of male beauty therapists as well as a growing number of male salon clients.

# Chapter Two

# Safety First

*Keep your salon a safe place for your clients, your colleagues and yourself.*

## Health and safety regulations

Health and safety regulations are so important that the government has brought in **legislation** to ensure your working environment is safe for you and your clients. The Health and Safety at Work Act 1974 defines employer responsibilities. These include providing a written safety policy. Make sure you understand important Health and Safety regulations such as:

- The Fire Precautions Act 1971. All staff must know their salon's fire safety procedures and regulations. Make sure you know how to use fire extinguishers for electrical and non-electrical fires.

> **Remember:** Only tackle a fire yourself if it is minor. Otherwise: *Get everyone out. Call the fire brigade out. And stay out.*

- The Control of Substances Hazardous to Health (COSHH) Regulations 1994 requires you to handle safely any substances that could damage your health.
- The Workplace (Health, Safety and Welfare) Regulations 1992 require spillages and breakages to be dealt with safely.

The 1995 Reporting of Injuries, Diseases and Dangerous Occurrences Regulations (RIDDOR) mean that certain accidents or injuries to staff or clients must be reported to the environmental health department of your **Local Authority** on a form available from **Her Majesty's Stationery Office** (HMSO – see Useful Addresses). Accidents and injuries that need to be reported include work injuries lasting more than three days, legionella, tetanus, hepatitis, occupational dermatitis, occupational asthma, skin cancer and hand/arm vibration syndrome.

Inspections are carried out by the **Local Authority Health and Safety Inspector**. A copy of current Health and Safety regulations is available from **HMSO**, see also Appendix.

# Local Authority hygiene regulations

These are known as **by-laws**. They are just as important as government **legislation**. They are drawn up and monitored by the **Local Authority** (also known as the **council**). As well as regulating general hygiene standards, **by-laws** also regulate some skin-piercing treatments.

> **Remember:** The law changes each time new acts of parliament and **by-laws** are introduced. The government expects you, as a professional, to keep up to date with changes throughout your career. It is illegal to break these regulations. Ignorance of the law is never accepted as an excuse.

Hygiene standards must be kept up to stop the spread of bloodborne infections such as hepatitis B, hepatitis C and HIV (the AIDS virus) as well as less serious infections. Inspections are carried out by the **Local Authority Health and Safety Inspector**.

Your salon should have a copy of current **Local Authority** regulations. If not, find your local Health Authority's address in your local phone directory and send off for one.

# Professional codes of conduct

A **code of conduct** is an agreement by members of a profession to behave professionally. Legal requirements cover the basic safeguards to life, professional **codes of conduct** cover less serious but equally important areas.

The term **best practice** is used to describe how the best professionals behave. For example, it is **best practice** to do a patch test before applying an eyelash tint. If you join a professional association such as The British Association of Beauty Therapists and Cosmetologists (**BABTAC**), you will be expected to keep to their professional **code of conduct**. Be sure to study and stick to your association's **code of conduct**.

> **Did you know?** Members of professional associations are so professional that the associations can offer their members comprehensive professional indemnity insurance at low rates. This means that arranging your professional insurance through your association can save you money.

It is not *illegal* to break a professional **code of conduct** but it will seriously damage your professional reputation. It may also mean your insurance is invalid. This means you risk being *personally* sued for any damage you cause to a client or colleague.

# Professional working practice

Take control of every treatment situation and always work safely and responsibly.

## Work safely in your salon

- Slips and trips are the most common cause of work-related accidents. Many salon preparations contain oil, fats and waxes. Spillages containing grease are the most hazardous. Make sure any spillage is thoroughly cleaned up; use plenty of detergent (washing-up liquid) because this breaks up grease. It is better to hold up a client or colleague while you clear up a greasy spillage than risk her slipping and badly injuring herself.

■ Arrange your salon and treatment cubicles to avoid trailing electrical cables. Coiled extension cables are safer because they stretch but don't trail along the floor.

■ Remember that heating wax is a fire hazard. Never leave a waxer heating overnight or in an empty salon.

■ When a fluorescent lighting tube begins to fail, it flickers. It will continue to give adequate light for a while but the flickering light can trigger attacks of migraine or epilepsy in susceptible people. Replace failing tubes quickly.

■ If you refill small fluid dispensers from larger bottles, make sure you use the correct fluid. Ensure the dispenser is clearly and correctly labelled. If initials such as S.S. are used for surgical spirit, for example, make sure you know what the initials stand for and remember to check the label on the large bottle for hazards or storage instructions.

■ Breakages happen. Occasionally, retail or salon stock breaks during transit. Safeguard yourself, your clients and your colleagues by making sure all glass fragments are safely cleared up; use rubber gloves and a vacuum cleaner.

■ Make sure you know how all salon facilities such as the sauna, spa bath or exercise machines work and how to use them safely. Ask for training if necessary.

**Figure 2.1** Only use electrical equipment when fully competent

## Work safely on clients

■ **Contra-indications** are indications against (contra) treatment. Always check for **contra-indications** before beginning a treatment. For example, electrical treatment using **high frequency** current can interfere with signals from a client's pacemaker (a device fitted internally to regulate heartbeat).

- Never give treatment that could cause long-term damage to your client's skin or nails. For example, when applying nail extensions, don't buff or dehydrate the natural nail more than necessary. Be careful not to make couperose skin – high colouring – worse with heat treatments.

- Always ask to attend professional training courses for treatments not covered in your basic training, such as eyelash perming.

- Never work over recent scars or surgical incisions.

- Always test hot wax, paraffin wax and warm wax on yourself before testing on your client. Make sure your client understands she is not to 'grin and bear' wax which is too hot.

- Never allow clients to exceed safe treatment limits. For example, government health representatives recommend no more than 20 sunbed sessions per year.

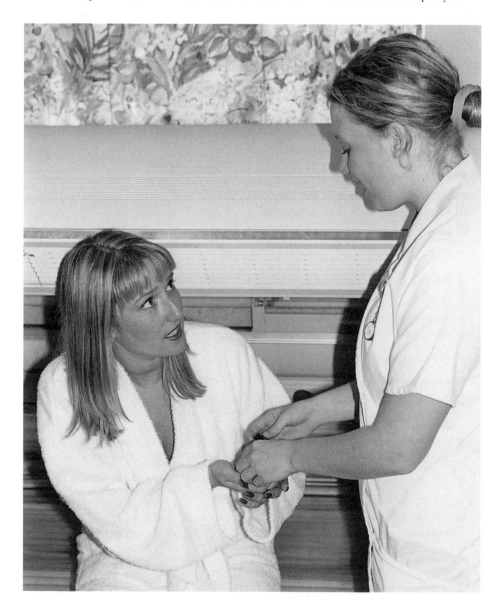

**Figure 2.2**
Ensure your client uses equipment safely, e.g. ensure she uses safety goggles.

■ Take particular care when working close to the eye area. For example, clients can flinch during **milia** removal. Explain that, for this reason you cannot remove **milia** too close to the eye.

■ Gently release pus from a pustular spot but never squeeze a pustular or blind spot. This can easily spread infection to the surrounding tissue and even into the bloodstream if the spot is near a prominent blood vessel. This can cause blood poisoning.

■ Apply nail extensions hygienically and keep a regular check on the health of your clients' nails; fungal infections can quickly gain a hold beneath loosening extensions.

■ Some aromatherapy oils are potentially **toxic**. Take care with aniseed, arnica, comfrey, mugwort, oreganum, penny royal, St John's wort, sassafras, sage, savory, tansy, thuja (pronounced thooya), wintergreen and wormwood.

## Work hygienically

Your salon and treatment rooms must look *and* be clean and hygienic.

> **Remember:** Everything that comes into contact with your client must *always* be clean and hygienic. After treatment:
> ■ Throw away disposable items such as emery boards.
> ■ Sterilize metal tools such as comedone extractors.
> ■ Wash brushes such as mask brushes.
> ■ Launder fabrics such as towels.

■ Sanitize all salon furniture by wiping over with a solution of disinfectant at least once a week.

■ Every client must have a freshly laundered gown and towels. Protect couch towels and covers with disposable paper bedroll to cut down on laundry.

■ Always cover pillows and bolsters with pillow slips. Change them regularly.

■ Store cotton wool and tissues in covered, hygienic containers.

■ Line treatment trolleys with disposable paper bedroll. Change this every few days or as necessary.

■ Regularly clean off wax splashes from the couch, trolley, wall and floor. Wax drips can land you with costly dry cleaning bills if wax gets onto your clients' clothes.

■ Use the waxer's lid to keep out dust and microbes. (If your waxer doesn't have a lid, use the lid from the pot of wax.)

■ Choose a waxer that is easy to keep clean – and keep it clean. To prevent wax build-up between each waxing, wipe off drips with a cotton wool pad, dampened with surgical spirit or specialist wax cleaner.

■ Dispose of your last client's epilated or waxed hairs so that they are out of sight of your next client. She will certainly find them a highly unpleasant sight!

■ To comply with health and safety regulations, all salon waste bins must have lids and be easy to clean (i.e. plastic not wicker). Line them with a disposable bin-liner. A large white plastic bin designed for the disposal of sanitary towels is ideal.

> **Remember:** Clean all wax residue from the bin and disinfect it regularly. An open bin, stained with blobs of eyelash tint, covered with wax and pubic hair will doubtless turn your client's stomach. Enough said?

## Use safe and hygienic tools

Always buy good-quality tools and equipment from a well-established beauty equipment supplier or wholesaler rather than the local chemist where quality can vary.

■ Invest in good quality manicure equipment and replace it as soon as it gets blunt. Blunt cuticle clippers will tear rather than cut cuticles, which could then become infected.

■ Toenails are much tougher than fingernails. Use clippers or specialized toenail scissors to trim them. Blunt toenail clippers can snap rather than cut toenails. This could leave your client's nail bed painfully exposed.

■ Poorly finished tweezers can scratch your client's skin, leaving it prone to infection. Don't use **electro-epilation** forceps for tweezing. The sharp, pointed ends can also graze.

■ Use a pre-packed sterile 'Microlance' for removing **milia**, not the pointed end of a comedone extractor or a sewing needle.

■ Poor-quality make-up brushes can shed hairs which can fall into your client's eyes or stick to lipstick.

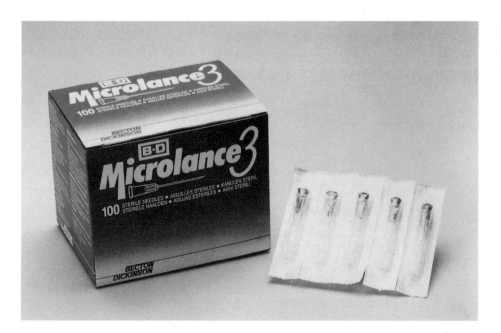

**Figure 2.3**
Microlances are ideal for extracting milia

- To avoid **cross-infection**, use disposable make-up brushes where practical, such as lip, mascara and eyeliner brushes.
- Cut the brushes off salon mascaras so that they are never accidentally used and then replaced in the tube. Mascaras quickly become contaminated, replace them every three months.
- Once you begin working, you will need two sets of tools: one in use and one being sterilized.

**Figure 2.4**
Glutaraldehyde
sterilizing fluid

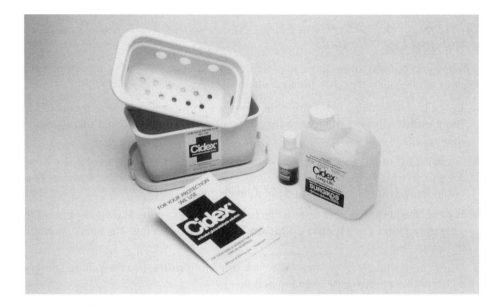

- A glass bead sterilizer is useful for sanitizing small, regularly used equipment such as tweezers and comedone extractors but may not destroy all **pathogens** completely.

**Figure 2.5**
A glass bead
sterilizer

## Use safe and hygienic equipment

Along with training, ask your tutor if you can also read the instruction booklet before using electrical salon equipment.

- All salon areas must be lit well enough to prevent client or staff accidents. Replace light bulbs in steam rooms, saunas and flotation tanks as soon as they fail. (Keep a stock of spare bulbs.)
- All electrical equipment must, by law, be 'properly maintained' under the Provision and Use of Work Equipment Regulations 1992 and regularly inspected under the Electricity at Work Regulations 1989.
- Ideally, attend a manufacturer's training course before using specialized electrical equipment.
- Use electrical body treatments with care; **galvanism** can burn and **vacuum suction** can bruise if misused.
- All wax heaters have in-built thermostats which prevent the wax becoming too hot. Always ensure the thermostat is set to the correct temperature and never use a waxer with a broken thermostat.
- Never heat paraffin wax in a depilatory wax heater since even the lowest setting will overheat the wax, which can cause a severe burn.
- Never leave a client unsupervised under a facial steamer.

## Never misuse products or equipment

Always follow the manufacturer's directions when using products and equipment.

- Salon ear-piercing guns are designed to pierce earlobes only. Never use them for specialized piercing such as ear cartilage, nose or other body parts. You will invalidate your insurance. For reasons of hygiene, specialized nose studs without butterfly clasps must be worn in the nose. (Cartilage is also more difficult to treat when infected.)
- Never use hairdressing products such as bleach, which are designed for the scalp, on your client's face or body.
- Keep treatment equipment solely for treatment use. For example, a gentian violet ear-piercing marker pen looks similar to a regular marker pen. Don't keep it at the reception desk!
- If your hot waxer has a sieve, throw it away. Never sieve and reuse hot wax. This is no longer considered safe because of the possibility of spreading infections such as hepatitis and HIV (AIDS).
- Never use a blade on your clients' feet. Never cut away hard skin or corns. This is a job for a qualified chiropodist.
- Use only distilled water in facial steamers. The salts in tap water can cause steamers to spit boiling water droplets at your client!

## High-risk treatments

In insurance terms, some salon treatments are regarded as high-risk treatments. These are the treatments which clients most often claim damages for. Your insurance will have special requirements for high-risk treatments. You may need a diploma from a recognized trainer to be insured to perform them. Ask for a photocopy of your salon's insurance specifications so that you can make sure you follow them correctly. High-risk treatments include:

- ear-piercing
- **electro-epilation**
- eyelash perming
- eyelash tinting
- galvanism for the body
- laser treatment
- **micropigmentation**
- paraffin wax treatment
- **red vein cauterization**
- waxing.

## Preventing folliculitis and infection

Ensure you give each client accurate and sufficient aftercare instructions, especially for high-risk treatments involving hair removal or skin piercing. Pus at the mouth of hair follicles means that, at some point after hair removal, the empty hair follicles became infected with bacteria. This is known as folliculitis and is more common in hot weather when perspiration easily washes bacteria into empty follicles. The same applies to ear-piercing.

It is often difficult to tell when the site became infected. If it happened at your salon, this is due to bad practice from unhygienic working methods and several clients may be affected. To prevent this, ensure hygiene standards are maintained:

- Swab the area to be treated with antiseptic or surgical spirit before treatment.
- Use a new waxing spatula for each client.
- Store waxing strips hygienically in a plastic bag.
- Ensure your afterwax lotion contains antiseptic.
- Ensure your client fully understands your aftercare instructions. Ideally, provide her with a printed aftercare sheet that she can study at home – some suppliers stock such sheets for this purpose.
- Ensure your client understands she must use her aftercare lotion for the recommended length of time.

If infection happened after your client left your salon, maybe you didn't give enough aftercare instructions. Explain to your client that empty follicles are prone to infection for 48 hours after treatment. Sources of infection include:

- waterborne bacteria, e.g. in baths and showers
- perspiration – extra care should be taken during hot weather
- bacteria on tight clothing, e.g. tights, socks or trousers
- bacteria in creams and lotions such as roll-on deodorant or body lotion.

## Accidents waiting to happen

When working with the public, it's a good idea to take a course in First Aid. Don't wait for an accident to happen before thinking about salon safety.

## *Recognising the 'near miss'*

Think back to your last 'near miss'. Maybe you tripped over a trailing cable or lost your footing on a wet patch on the floor. Hopefully, you didn't hurt yourself. A 'near miss' is a situation that could have caused an accident but luckily did not. A responsible person who has a 'near miss' will think, *'What can I do to stop that happening again. Next time, I may not be so lucky.'*

At work (and at home) think of every 'near miss' as an accident waiting to happen. Change the set-up so that the accident can no longer happen to you, your colleagues or your clients.

## *Thinking ahead*

You don't have to wait for a 'near miss'. Think ahead to what accidents may happen in your salon.

- Lamp bulbs can shatter as they are switched on. Always switch on a **UV** or **IR** lamp *before* positioning it over your client.
- Many manicure products are flammable. Never allow your client to smoke at the manicure station.
- Place a warning sign over floors that have been recently mopped.
- Place a non-slip mat in the shower.

# *When things go wrong*

'Negligence' means carelessness. There is no excuse for professional negligence. But all professionals make mistakes from time to time. It's not the end of the world, although it may feel like it for a while. It's okay to make a mistake – just don't make the same one twice.

Mistakes can happen from lack of experience at the beginning of careers. Unfortunately, this is also the time when you feel least equipped to deal with mistakes. Professional employers and experienced therapists will be aware of this and be supportive of newly qualified professionals.

## *Mistakes*

If you make a mistake during treatment that you can't put right, don't be tempted to pretend it hasn't happened and hope your client won't notice. She will. See the situation as an opportunity to show your professionalism. Calmly explain what went wrong and apologize (once). For example, if you cause a bruise during waxing, say: 'I've caused a small bruise here. I do apologize. It's nothing to worry about and will fade during the next few days. I can give you some cover cream if you think the bruise may be a nuisance to you.' Explain that there will be no charge for the treatment. For best customer relations, a good employer should agree that charging for substandard treatment is unprofessional.

If the mistake is more serious, such as a wax burn, don't wait to see if your client complains. Advise her to visit her GP if she is at all concerned about the injury and compensate her with gift vouchers or retail goods. Phone her the following day and show concern. You can even send flowers by way of an apology, if you feel this is warranted. These measures show that mistakes are rare in your salon since you'd soon go out of business if you did this regularly.

Most clients will accept your apology. They may even be impressed by the professional way you handled the situation and will probably continue to be your client.

## Admitting liability

Insurance companies generally advise professionals never to 'admit liability' – this means admitting to a mistake. This is because insurance companies hope that professional negligence can't be proved so that they can avoid paying compensation and keep premiums low. While cost-effective for the insurance company, this approach ignores the fact that most people don't want to cash in on mistakes. They simply want to be treated fairly.

Often, all a dissatisfied client wants is an explanation, reassurance and an apology. If you feel happier not 'admitting liability', don't say a general 'sorry'; say that you are 'sorry your client is dissatisfied'. This is called a 'qualified apology' and means you do not accept blame.

## Clients who sue

Sometimes clients sue professionals when they are mistreated. This is becoming more common. For example, your client could sue you for 'loss of enjoyment' during her holiday if you bruise her bikini-line. If you have no insurance, this could cost your salon – or you personally – thousands of pounds in compensation and legal fees.

Always remember that the final decision to give treatment rests with you, the therapist. This is because you have received the training and gained the expertise to know whether treatment may damage your client. If your client asks for a treatment which you believe is unsuitable, it is your duty as a professional to refuse treatment, no matter how insistent your client is.

> **Remember:** Never be fooled by a client telling you she will take full responsibly for you performing an unsuitable or **contra-indicated** treatment. Legally, responsibility remains with you, even if your client signs a disclaimer. *Never perform a treatment against your better judgement.*

## Insurance

If you do not arrange personal professional indemnity insurance through a professional association such as **BABTAC**, check that your employer has sufficient professional indemnity insurance which covers you.

- Public Liability Insurance is highly recommended for salon owners. It insures against becoming personally liable to pay compensation for injury to clients and damage to clients' property in the salon.
- Product Liability Insurance covers damage or injury to clients from branded salon products. This insurance is not valid if you sell or give your client products you mix yourself such as aromatherapy oils, or if you repackage branded products.
- Treatment Risk Insurance covers damage or injury to clients where the therapist or treatment was not at fault, such as an unforeseen allergic reaction.

None of the above insurances is compulsory but they bring peace of mind and are excellent value if you need to claim when a client sues.

It's not necessary to display insurance certificates in your salon, although it's a good idea to display certificates of qualification and membership of professional associations so that your clients can see that you hold professional qualifications and are a member of a professional body.

## Quiz – How professional are you?

1. *Mrs P has chronic seborrhoea, which her consultant dermatologist has failed to improve. You regularly wax her eyebrows. She notices that exfoliation improves her skin condition. She pleads with you to wax her entire face. Do you:*

   a) Agree to wax her face because you feel sorry for her and she is desperate for some improvement to her skin condition?

   b) Politely explain that depilatory wax is not intended for exfoliation and suggest she book a paraffin wax facial instead because this wax is more suitable for facial exfoliation?

   c) Do it to see if it works; you may discover a new treatment and become famous?

2. *Mrs F, a high-powered business woman, books a course of mechanical massage treatment because she is desperate to reduce her thighs before her exotic holiday. During the consultation, you learn that she has had phlebitis. You recognize phlebitis as a contra-indication to mechanical massage. You tell Mrs F that unfortunately you will not be able to perform the treatment. Mrs F is furious. She threatens to take her business elsewhere. Do you:*

   a) Agree to perform the slimming treatment because she's quite scary and you're worried about getting into trouble with your manager?

   b) Politely explain that you can't perform any treatment affecting her circulation because it may dislodge a blood clot that could be dangerous for her health?

   c) Do the course of treatments because you need the commission and the chances of the clot lodging in her brain, lungs or heart are probably less than 50 per cent?

3. *Miss L is getting married tomorrow. A booking mistake has been made with her appointment. She comes straight off the sunbed for a leg wax. You apologize for the mistake and explain you cannot wax her legs immediately after a heat treatment. Miss L insists you perform the treatment, saying she will take full responsibility. Do you:*

   a) Agree to wax her legs? After all, you can't send her down the aisle hairy!

   b) Explain that waxing straight after a heat treatment could remove a thin layer of skin and this will look worse than the hair. Suggest a trainee perform a complementary pedicure and wax her legs later when they have cooled sufficiently?

   c) Wax her legs while she's standing in front of the open fridge?

4. *Mr K asks you to pierce his tongue. You explain you do not have suitable equipment or insurance for body piercing but he comes back several times during the day and makes a fuss in the salon each time. Do you:*

   a) Agree to do it although you are a bit nervous. You have to gain experience somehow.

Quiz continued

b) Politely but firmly refuse giving the address of a reputable licensed body piercer.

c) Say you'll do it, but practice on the trainee first. Mr K is quite good-looking and you want to look like you know what you're doing.

5. *Mrs W arrives for her sunbed treatment sunburned. You explain she cannot have her treatment. She gets very upset and explains that this is the very reason she needs the treatment. She is going to a dinner and dance that evening and needs to cover the red burn with brown tan. Do you:*

a) Let her use the sunbed because she starts to cry and you feel really mean?

b) Politely but firmly refuse her treatment?

c) Let her use the sunbed, it's been a long day and you can't be bothered to argue with her?

## Answers

**If you chose 'a's** – Don't be a wimp when it comes to professional negligence. *Never* perform a treatment that could damage your client.

**If you chose 'b's** – Well done, you are a true professional.

**If you chose 'c's** – Aghhh! The therapist from hell!

# Chapter Three

# Professional Salon Reception

*An unskilled receptionist can lose business; a skilled receptionist can create business.*

## Reception

Large beauty salons, health clubs and health farms usually employ receptionists. Smaller salons can't always employ a separate receptionist. The role of salon receptionist is vital. If you are receptionist, you represent the salon, all its staff and all their skills. You can't become a successful beauty therapist, salon manager or salon owner without good reception skills. They are vital to your career in beauty.

There is much job satisfaction to be gained from being an efficient receptionist. You'll need:

- a neat and tidy appearance
- a pleasant manner
- good communication skills
- a good telephone manner
- keyboard skills
- clear handwriting
- a willingness to learn
- to be able to work on your own initiative.

## The receptionist's role

Being a receptionist means much more than simply sitting behind a desk, pointing clients in the right direction. As receptionist, you will need to develop 'initiative'. To 'initiate' something means 'to start' something. Having initiative means being able to notice that things need doing and doing them competently without being prompted by your colleagues.

As receptionist, you can make a big difference to the smooth running of your salon. It may not be obvious to other staff when you are doing a good job but salon organization will quickly break down if you are not.

**Figure 3.1**
Smile, even when
on the phone!

> **Remember:** As a receptionist, think 'good manners' and you won't go far wrong.

## Representing the salon

Your salon will never get a second chance to make a first impression. First impressions colour our view forever. When a prospective client comes into – or phones – your salon, the first person she communicates with is the receptionist. If she is made to feel uncomfortable in any way, she won't stay long enough to find out how skilled the other staff are.

Beauty salons represent appearance and image. As a professional salon receptionist, you must always look good. Be aware of your non-verbal communication (also known as **body language**). Develop a calm manner and avoid nervous habits such as chewing gum, twirling round on your chair or fiddling with pencils.

## The reception area

Take charge of the reception area.

■ Keep reception furniture and office equipment clean, tidy and dust-free.

> **Did you know?** Wax-based furniture polish is not suitable for plastic-cased equipment such as phones, cash desks and keyboards. Use a soap-based cleaner which removes greasy deposits that look unsightly and can harbour germs.

- Arrange attractive displays in reception and the salon window. (Use empty boxes from salon **consumables** for window displays.)
- Check that magazines are up-to-date and in good condition.
- Look after pot plants or flower arrangements.
- It's best if staff don't sit and chat in groups at reception. Suggest that trainees, work experience pupils or therapists who aren't busy sit in the staff room.
- Advise the staff member responsible for reordering salon stationery when it runs low.

## Handling money

> **Remember:** Missing money is the receptionist's responsibility. Never leave an unlocked till unattended, even for a moment.

To avoid money discrepancies, be strict about keeping to the petty cash system. Don't let anyone take money from the till without replacing it with a petty cash receipt. If you need to take money from the till to buy small **consumables** such as polish or stamps, always ask first.

On reception, you will need to be able to:

- Give correct change to cash payment.
- Operate your till or cash desk correctly.
- Write down sales – your till may record this information. If not, note down sales on a 'sales docket', or on the appointment book. This information is needed to check stock levels.
- Accept payment by credit card correctly and know how to phone the credit card company for authorization if needed.
- Handle queries over cheques and credit cards discreetly. For example, if authorization for a credit card transaction is refused, take your client aside to explain this privately.
- Be discreetly on the lookout for fraud.
- Accept payment by cheque and cheque card. Always copy the card number onto the back of the cheque, even when you know the client.
- Know company policy for handling a disagreement over change. If you have time, 'cash up' while the client waits, to see if there is extra cash in the till. If there isn't time, take the client's phone number and tell her you will ring her to let her know later that day.

> **Remember:** If your client pays by cheque or credit card, a quick glance at the card will tell you her name. As you hand the card back, you can say: 'Thank you, Mrs Brown.' New clients especially appreciate this personal touch.

## Assisting the therapist with treatment

Thoughtful receptionists and beauty assistants are greatly treasured by busy therapists. The more helpful you are, the more time your therapist will have to devote to your training. You can help your therapist by:

- Replacing the bedroll and tidying the couch between clients. You can do this if your therapist takes payment from her previous client herself.
- Setting out equipment before treatment.
- Keeping equipment tidy and clean, for example the wax heater.
- **Patch testing** for eyelash tinting and bleaching.
- Attending to distraught manicure clients who have smudged their polish after the therapist has begun treatment on her next client.
- Assisting with electronic muscle stimulation treatment by checking on the client, or – after training – removing the pads at the end of treatment.

## Looking after your clients

> **Remember:** As soon as a client enters your salon, she is your responsibility until you hand her over to a therapist's care.

### Greeting clients

Always show a polite interest in your clients. Ask their surnames politely. Add an appropriate title such as Miss, Mrs or Mr before the surname unless they invite you to use their first names.

- Some older clients feel uncomfortable being called by their first names.
- A discreet glance at your client's wedding ring finger may help you decide whether to use Miss or Mrs.
- Never use her treatment in place of her name. Never ask: 'Are you the bikini-line wax?'

Your greeting will depend on your salon and your client. Greetings can range from the very formal, 'Good morning, Madam. How may I help you?' to the very informal, 'Hi there, Suzy. What can we do for you today?'

Whichever greeting you decide is appropriate, even when you are busy, always acknowledge your client with a nod and a smile as soon as you see her, just as you would a friend.

### Client care

Caring for your client may include:

- Helping her on with her coat, showing her where to put a dripping umbrella, or finding a safe place for her shopping while she's in treatment
- Offering refreshments before or after treatment
- Chatting casually to your client to make her feel welcome
- Discreetly directing your client to the lavatory
- Offering your client a magazine or salon literature while she waits for treatment.

## Being helpful to clients

An efficient receptionist can help her clients get the best from treatment.

- Invite your manicure client to pay before treatment so that she doesn't smudge her nail polish while searching for her purse in her handbag.

> **Remember:** It's unprofessional to delve into your client's handbag because her nails are wet, even if invited!

- Suggest to a client who books a pedicure that she should wear sandals so that her toenail polish doesn't smudge.
- Ask male massage clients to bring along a pair of loose shorts to change into.
- If a new client books a bikini-line wax for her holiday, suggest she bring along her bikini or swimsuit.

## Dealing with delays

A good receptionist makes a client's wait seem as short as possible. Salon appointments can sometimes be delayed. Keep a check on waiting clients' appointment times. Apologize for any delay and reassure the client she will be seen soon. She will then be much happier to wait. If there is a delay of more than ten minutes, try to find out why, but don't disturb a therapist in treatment.

## Provide refreshments

If your friend visits you at home, you offer a drink to be sociable, not because you think she is thirsty. Drinks do more than quench people's thirst. They make people feel welcomed and cared-for. If your salon is pleasant and relaxing, clients may stay to relax after treatment or arrive early and enjoy flicking through a glossy magazine with some refreshment. To save asking each time how your client takes her drinks, you can note it in pencil on her record card. Refreshments are also useful for occupying clients if treatment is delayed.

Therapists are generally too busy to make refreshments, so take charge of providing refreshments and of the washing-up! Always serve drinks in appropriate crockery. Serve cold drinks in a clean glass. Serve hot drinks in a clean cup with saucer (or mug). Don't forget to offer sugar from a separate sugar bowl.

## Client confidentiality

In salons, clients' personal details are recorded on **record cards** (sometimes called **consultation cards**) or on computer files. Client confidentiality must be maintained at all times. Never leave a client's **record card** lying around where other clients may see it. Client information must never be copied or passed on in any form. Never give any information about a client to anyone, in person or over the phone. This includes:

- whether or not a celebrity visits the salon
- clients' business or home phone numbers or addresses
- information about treatments booked by clients.

If you break this rule, you will be guilty of gross **misconduct** and open to prosecution under the Data Protection Act of 1998. This could result in instant dismissal.

## Handling complaints

If something goes wrong, it's likely that you will be the first person on hand that a dissatisfied client will complain to. Problems and complaints you may have to deal with include:

- a booking discrepancy, for example two clients booked in at the same time with the same therapist
- a complaint about treatment
- a complaint about a product.

For tips on handling complaints, see Chapter Seven, Act Professionally.

# Appointments

As receptionist, you will have charge of the appointment book (sometimes called a reception book). You may be responsible for drawing up the new one. As well as columns for each therapist, your appointment book will need columns for equipment that can be booked, such as sunbeds and steam baths.

Clients can easily see the appointment book, so like the reception area, keep it neat and tidy and free from doodles. Make bookings in pencil because these are easily altered.

It's more profitable for your salon if you can fit short appointments into gaps between existing ones. This leaves more space for longer bookings. It makes sense to offer your client an appointment that suits the salon; she'll soon tell you if it doesn't suit her.

If your salon pays commission on treatment, remember that the therapists' wages depend on the size of their **clientele**. This means therapists will probably be keen to treat their clients personally.

## Booking an appointment professionally

- Greet your client with a smile – even on the phone.
- Ask which appointment she would like to book.
- Ask when she would like her appointment, turn to the correct page and offer her a suitable time. She may suggest a specific time.
- Ask if she wants a particular therapist to treat her.
- Write the name of the treatment in the correct column with the correct therapist and block out the allotted treatment time.
- Ask for the client's surname. Write this in the correct column alongside the treatment. If she only offers her first name, politely explain that you need her surname to avoid confusion.
- Ask for the client's daytime telephone number and STD (area) code. Write this alongside her name. You may need to contact the client about her appointment and her telephone number on file may not be up-to-date.

> **Did you know?** As you are training, you may make a mistake and need to ring your client back to alter an appointment. If this happens, it is very useful to have her telephone number. If you make a booking mistake and forget to take her number, immediately dial 1471. This will give you the number of the last person to phone the salon.

- Confirm the day, time, therapist and treatment with your client to avoid confusion.
- Write these details on an appointment card and give it to your client, if she is present.

Record each client's arrival in the appointment book by drawing a diagonal line through her name. Record her departure by crossing through this line. This way, therapists know for safety reasons who has arrived and who is in the salon (e.g. in case of a fire).

Be discreet about naming your client's treatment in front of others. It's best never to mention electrolysis in reception where other clients can overhear.

## Patch testing

Some people are allergic to the chemical **toluenediamine** in eyelash tint. When you book an eyelash tint appointment, ask whether your client has recently had the tint at your salon. If she has not, explain that she will need a **patch test** 48 hours beforehand, to check for allergy, even if she has been tested or treated elsewhere.

Once you have been trained to give the test, you can perform it yourself. Do the test behind the ear rather than in the crook of the arm; tint quickly stains clothing. Always remember to record the test and results on your client's record card.

Patch tests are also recommended for bleaching and **micropigmentation** and can be made for any treatment where the client or therapist is concerned about an allergic reaction.

## Spotting booking mistakes

Both your colleagues and your clients depend on you to make appointments correctly. Just one wrongly booked appointment can:

- Throw the whole salon into chaos.
- Ruin a client's wedding or holiday or both.
- Tarnish the good reputation of your salon.
- Lose your salon money.
- Lose your salon clients.

Check through appointments a few days ahead, to spot booking mistakes early. Things to look out for include:

- The day or date has been wrongly copied into the appointment book.
- An appointment is booked on a day when the salon is closed, such as a bank holiday.
- An appointment is booked with a therapist who will be absent at the time.

- A treatment is booked with a therapist who doesn't perform that treatment.
- The wrong amount of time has been booked for the treatment.
- One set of equipment is booked for simultaneous appointments.
- Incompatible treatments are booked, such as a wax treatment followed by a heat treatment.
- A booking discrepancy, for example a client has two closely booked, identical appointments. This may be because she altered her appointment and the unwanted one was not erased. Phone to check which one is correct.

## Salon abbreviations

For speed, salons use abbreviations to book treatments into the appointment book. If you are unsure of the abbreviation, write out the treatment in full. Missed appointments are shown by either ANK – 'appointment not kept' or DNA – 'did not attend'. C stands for 'cancellation'. If there is still time to rebook the appointment, the booking is erased. Sometimes there are oblique strokes between the letters such as F/F which stands for full facial. Check for variations used in your salon.

## Client record cards

As receptionist, you can help your salon run smoothly by taking out **client record cards** for the next day's appointments and refiling cards from the previous day.

You can help your therapist by inviting new clients to fill out their name and address on a client **record card** while they wait for treatment. This also gives the waiting client something to do.

**Record cards** are filed alphabetically, by the client's surname. It is important that cards are filed correctly. A 'lost' card may mean searching through the whole filing system.

**Figure 3.2**
Client record cards

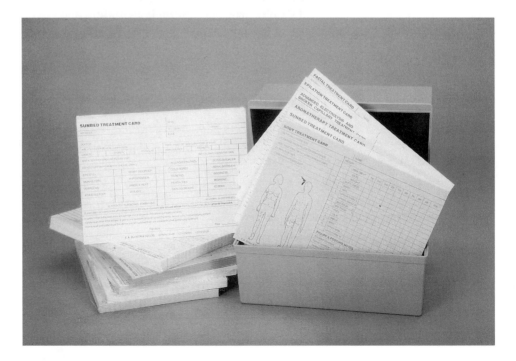

**Table 3.1**

Salon treatment
abbreviations

| *Abbreviation* | *Treatment* |
| --- | --- |
| **Facial treatments** | |
| FF | Full facial |
| EF or brand of facial such as Cathiodermie or CACI | Electrical facial |
| CMUp | Cleanse and make-up |
| BMup | Bridal make-up |
| MupL | Make-up lesson |
| ELT | Eyelash tint |
| ELP | Eyelash perm |
| EBT | Eyebrow tint (or sometimes Eyebrow trim or tidy) |
| EBS | Eyebrow shape |
| **Epilation** | |
| FLW | Full leg wax |
| $\frac{1}{2}$ LW or $\frac{1}{2}$ wax | Half leg wax |
| $\frac{3}{4}$ LW or $\frac{3}{4}$ wax | Three-quarter leg wax |
| BLW | Bikini-line wax |
| UAW | Under-arm wax |
| FAW | Forearm wax |
| LW | Lip wax |
| LB | Lip bleach |
| EE or EL | **Elecro-epilation** or electrolysis |
| **Manicure and pedicure** | |
| MAN | Manicure |
| PED | Pedicure |
| RPol or RVan | Repolish or Revarnish |
| F MAN | French manicure |
| PW MAN | Paraffin wax manicure |
| PW PED | Paraffin wax pedicure |
| Nail Ex | Nail extensions |
| **Massage and body treatment** | |
| BNM | Back and neck massage |
| FBM | Full body massage |
| LM | Leg massage |
| AM | Aromatherapy massage |
| G5 | Gyratory vibrator/mechanical massage (the abbreviation is a brand name for a gyratory vibrator with 5 heads). |
| S/Tone or S/T | Electronic muscle stimulator or exerciser (the abbreviation stands for Slendertone which is a brand name for a faradic machine). |
| **Other treatments** | |
| EP | Ear-pierce |
| MP/SPM | Micropigmentation/semi-permanent make-up |
| Cons | Consultation |

- If two clients have the same surname such as Smith, file Angela Smith in front of Betty Smith, using their first names alphabetically.
- Hyphenated surnames are filed under the first half of the surname.
- Surnames with prefixes such as Du, De, Von, Van, La, Le and O' are filed as if the prefix forms part of the main name.
- Surnames beginning with Mc are filed as if they are spelt Mac.
- Surnames beginning with the prefix St. are filed as if they are spelt Saint.

## Therapists in treatment

It's considered unprofessional for a therapist to leave her client once treatment has started, particularly during massage treatment. Never interrupt a client's treatment to ask the therapist a question or tell her she has a visitor or phone call unless it is very urgent or an emergency. Explain to the caller that the therapist is 'in treatment' and offer to take a message. It's fine to interrupt treatment with a message for the *client*.

Some salons communicate through **intercoms**. Keep **intercom** communications to a minimum when the therapist is in treatment. Use your initiative; you can get away with briefly interrupting a manicure but not a massage. Some therapists switch off the **intercom** during massage treatment.

# Additional reception duties

## Handling general enquires

Not all visitors to reception will be clients for beauty treatment. Some will be **walk-ins**, people who come into your salon from the street to enquire about treatment or to browse or buy products. Use your common sense for when you can deal with an enquiry from a **walk-in** and when you need information or support from another member of staff.

Prospective clients will ask all sorts of questions about your salon and its treatments. Be patient and helpful. Never give the impression of being rushed – particularly on the phone. If the prospective client asks questions about treatment which are too technical for you to answer, offer her a **consultation** (a 10–15 minute appointment) with a qualified therapist. Explain this will be free of charge. Other salon visitors you will need to deal with include:

- business representatives (sometimes known as **reps**)
- officials such as the **Health and Safety Inspector**
- job-hunters.

Politely find out who your visitor is and the reason for their visit before telling your manager.

## Selling products

Clients will ask your advice about products as well as treatments, so you will need to learn about your salon's range of skin care products and cosmetics. You may earn commission on sales. You can also be very helpful to a busy therapist by taking charge of her client after treatment and helping her choose or pay for retail products.

## Taking messages

Copy down messages correctly and pass them to the person in question as soon as possible. Be sure to record the following information:

- name of the caller
- telephone number of the caller
- who the message is for
- the message itself
- whether a reply is needed
- the date and time you took the message
- your name as receiver of the message.

## Supervising wet room and sunbed treatments

As receptionist, you may also be trained to supervise clients for wet room or sun tanning treatment. You will need to explain how to use the facilities and see that the facilities are used correctly. For example, ensure that clients shower before treatment.

Check that your clients have no **contra-indications** to the treatment and make sure they fill out client **record cards** correctly.

## Receiving stock

As receptionist, you will need to sign for packages delivered to your salon. When a package arrives that is addressed to the salon:

- Sign for the package and write 'unchecked' next to your signature. This means you haven't checked the contents.
- Store the package safely so that neither colleagues nor clients trip over it.

> **Remember:** If the package looks heavy, think ahead and ask the delivery person to place it in a suitable place straight away.

- Carefully unpack the contents during a quiet time at reception.
- Find the invoice inside, which lists the contents. Tick every item off on the invoice, checking that the supplier has packed the correct quantity. Tell your manager immediately if anything is missing or damaged.
- Make sure the packing is completely empty before you dispose of it.
- Price up and display the retail products. Always check with your manager if you are not sure of the price of a retail product.

Most skincare products and cosmetics have a limited **shelf-life**. This means they only last a certain length of time. This time is sometimes indicated by the **use-by date**. **Stock rotation** means placing new stock behind older stock so that this is sold first. The stock rotation mnemonic (something that helps you remember) is **FIFO**. This stands for 'First In, First Out'.

You may be asked to make weekly stock checks so that your manager will know when salon retail stocks are running low.

## Stock storage and display

Make sure salon consumables are correctly stored. For example, heat and light can quickly destroy the effectiveness of aromatherapy oils and hydrogen peroxide used to tint eyelashes. This is why unstable substances such as hydrogen peroxide are supplied in brown glass bottles to protect them from light damage.

- Handle retail packaging carefully. Boxes are easily scuffed. The glamour of an expensively packaged product will be destroyed if the packaging is damaged.
- Protect the packaging from strong sunlight. Faded packaging gives the impression that the stock is old.
- Protect the package from soiling. Check that nothing can leak onto retail stock during storage.
- Product displays shouldn't look untouched. Products should look as though they are selling!

## Supervising clients' children

During the school holidays, a responsible receptionist can be an invaluable help in the salon, supervising clients' children while clients are having treatment. A beauty salon can be a dangerous place for young children but sometimes their presence is unavoidable.

> **Remember:** Always put child safety before client care.

When supervising small children in a beauty salon, your first priority is to keep them safe. If you can also manage to answer the phone and serve clients, well done! It's useful to keep a book, puzzle or toy behind the reception desk to help keep young children amused.

# In at the deep end

Beauty salons are very busy places. Qualified staff will be busy treating clients. Experienced trainees will be assisting. This often means that the newest trainee is left on reception. You may be given the role formally or you may need to step in as receptionist at a moment's notice.

Sometimes you may be asked to do things before you have been trained. Initiative is an excellent quality in a receptionist but don't take on more than you can handle. For example, a credit card payment is easy to take providing you know how. A mistake due to lack of training could prove expensive for the salon as well as damaging to your confidence. Explain to colleagues that you haven't been trained for the task but that you are willing to help as far as possible.

### What do you think?

1. Visit some salons and make a general inquiry. What type of reception did you get? Were you made to feel welcome? Would you recommend the salon to a friend?

2. Which characteristics of a professional receptionist are character traits and which can be learned?

# Chapter Four

# *Look After Yourself*

*To give the best to your clients, you must start out fit and healthy and stay that way.*

## *Working comfortably*

Salon treatment rooms and cubicles can be small, even cramped. Time spent arranging an efficient layout for your working area will save you time as well as effort during treatment. For example, arrange your manicure station and equipment so that you are not perched uncomfortably or reaching awkwardly. This is particularly important if you are left-handed and need a different working layout from your right-handed colleagues.

As soon as you begin work, make sure that your working routines do you no physical damage. This means you should be able to sit, stand, bend and stretch without straining or stressing muscles or ligaments. You should have 11 cubic metres of space to work in at the very least. (That's about 4 1/2 square metres. The cubic size of your working space = width of room × length of room × height of room.)

If you are too cramped to work comfortably, the quality of your treatments will suffer. Discuss this with your employer, who may consider altering permanent fittings such as store cupboards to improve your workspace.

> **Remember:** Never ignore muscular stiffness, numbness or pain. This is an early warning sign that damage may follow. Think about the way you work now.

## *Adequate working conditions and equipment*

Treatment rooms shouldn't be airless or dimly lit. Good lighting is essential for effective waxing and **electro-epilation** treatment. Check that your working conditions meet the requirements of the Workplace (Health, Safety and Welfare) Regulations Act 1992. Ask your employer for basic improvements if you need them.

Salon workers are prone to developing varicose veins, an unsightly and painful condition of the legs. This is because they do much of their work standing up. Unlike hairdressers, beauty therapists are able to sit down during some treatments. Make the most of this advantage and, where practical, sit rather than stand.

Under the Workplace Regulations Act 1992, your employer must provide a stool if it is appropriate for you to use one – during facial treatment for example. Your employer would rather invest in equipment than have you suffer costly industrial injury, for example, from bending at an awkward angle because you don't have a suitable stool. If you fail to ask for suitable equipment and then suffer injury at work, you may not be able to claim compensation.

■ Ideally, your stool will be height-adjustable with a backrest and castors. These help you move easily round the couch or from couch to work surface during treatment.

**Figure 4.1**
An adjustable
therapist's chair

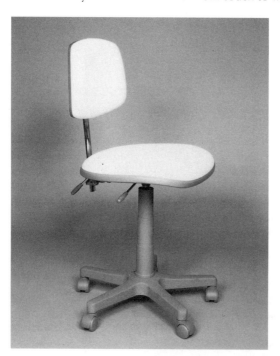

■ Your couch should be at a comfortable height. As a rough guide, your knuckles should rest on the couch when you stand beside it. You may need a height-adjustable couch if you are taller than average. If you use a portable couch weighing more than 13kg, it should have wheels to help you move it.

■ Couches fitted with bedroll dispensers cut out much reaching and bending.

■ If you need access to both sides of the couch, for example during **electro-epilation**, always remember to move it into position before the client arrives. Never attempt to move the couch while the client is lying on it.

■ Free-standing or trolley-mounted inspection lamps are more flexible than wall-mounted lamps.

■ An **intercom** connection between reception and treatment rooms is very useful for saving time and energy.

Having to work with unsuitable or insufficient equipment can cause you stress. If you lack basic equipment, discuss this with your employer, explaining why the equipment or products you need will improve service to clients.

# Sickness and unemployment

By law your employer will deduct a payment called **National Insurance** from your wage and pass this on to the government. (It is the only deduction, apart from income tax and pension contributions, that your employer may legally take from your wage.) **National Insurance** contributions entitle you to claim state benefits such as sickness benefit, unemployment benefit, maternity benefit and, eventually, a pension.

Your **National Insurance** contributions are shown on a form called a 'P60', which your employer will give you at the end of the tax year in April. Be sure you receive a correctly filled out P60 from your employer every year so that you can check that the government has received your **National Insurance** contributions from your employer. Keep your P60s safe; you may have to send them to your Social Security Office if you need to claim benefit. It's also advisable to keep your wage slips.

If you are self-employed, consider taking out personal health insurance in case accident or illness prevents you from working.

# Salon health hazards

All professions have hazards. Workers are responsible for their own conduct and welfare but under the Employers' Liability (Compulsory Insurance) Regulations 1969, employers must also insure their employees against accident and ill health resulting from their work. Find your salon's insurance certificate. It should be clearly displayed somewhere in your salon.

Never copy a colleague's unhygienic or unsafe working practices. If you are asked to do something which could cause you or someone else damage or injury, politely and tactfully explain your safety concerns. If this fails:

- Use one of your beauty therapy textbooks to help make your point. If this fails:
- Contact your local **Citizens' Advice Bureau (CAB)**. They can offer support and advice on employees' rights and health and safety rules. There is no charge. Find them in the *Yellow Pages*. For more information refer to the Control of Substances Hazardous to Health Act 1994 (COSHH)

## Avoiding infection

As an electrologist or beauty therapist, you must protect your clients from the risk of **cross-infection**. Equally importantly, you must protect yourself.

## Treatments involving body fluid

Serious bloodborne diseases such as hepatitis B, C and HIV – the AIDS virus – can be passed on through body fluids. However, this is extremely rare in beauty treatment because the amount of fluid in question is tiny. You may encounter small amounts of body fluids during the following treatments:

- You may release pus from a pustule.
- A **milium** or large **comedone** extraction may produce a small spot of blood or **plasma**.
- Waxed hair follicles may weep a small amount of **plasma**.
- The follicles of strong **terminal hair** such as under-arm and bikini-line hair can leak a little blood after waxing.

**Table 4.1** Avoid injury at work

| Source of risk or injury | Action |
| --- | --- |
| **Lower back injury** | You'll often need to bend over clients during treatment. Sit or stand as close as possible to the area you are treating to avoid over-stretching. Avoid hunching your shoulders and keep your back fairly straight when leaning forward. When standing, support the weight of your upper body on parted feet in what is known as 'walk stand' position. Take up a muscle-strengthening exercise such as swimming. |
| **Allergies such as contact dermatitis** | Like hairdressers, beauty therapists are at high risk of developing **contact dermatitis**. This condition can make working extremely difficult. It can ruin successful careers. As far as possible, keep chemicals such as surgical spirit and acetone off your skin. Use a barrier cream if your hands are sensitive to certain chemicals. Be careful with chemicals marked with a black cross on an orange background. Constant hand-washing and poor drying can also trigger dermatitis. Keep your hands in good condition and treat any dryness immediately. If necessary, visit your GP. Don't wait to develop symptoms. Prevention is better than cure. Once contact dermatitis gets a grip, it can be extremely difficult to cure. |
| **Repetitive strain injury (RSI)** | Numbness or pain in your arms or fingers may be a sign of injury from continuously repeating arm, hand or finger movements, for example during **electro-epilation** or massage. RSI is more common in therapists who specialize in these treatments. If performing any single treatment gives you pain, try to vary your work and see your GP. |
| **Vibration** | This is a deep massage movement where you place your fingertips in contact with your client and tense your arm muscles to produce a tremor. Performing this massage movement regularly could cause RSI so it's best not to do it. Mechanical hand-held massagers could have a similar effect if used excessively. |
| **Powders** | Powders such as talcum powder and chemicals in powders such as acrylic nail powder can irritate your lungs if inhaled. When handling powders, don't allow clouds of powder to fill the air. Avoid breathing powders in. |
| **Flammable products** | Never allow clients to smoke near flammable chemicals such as **volatile** manicure products. |
| **UV rays and radiant heat lamps** | **UV** rays are radiated from sunbeds and solaria. **IR** rays are radiated from radiant heat lamps. **UV** rays are **carcinogenic** and both UV and **IR** rays can cause **cataracts**. During treatment, staff and clients must wear protective goggles. Anyone in the area must be protected from **UV** and **IR** rays. This means that sunbed or heat ray lamps should not be visible to the receptionist as she sits at reception. Don't exceed safe tanning limits. Excessive **UV** exposure can trigger skin cancer and will certainly age skin prematurely – neither is a good outcome for a professional beauty therapist! |
| **Steam** | Visible steam has air mixed with it, which cools it. **True steam** is invisible and scalding hot. Scalds can be serious and more painful than burns. Keep your face, arms and hands well away from the mouth of a working steamer. |

| Source of risk or injury | Action |
|---|---|
| **Ozone** | Ozone is produced through a **UV** light fitted into some facial steamers. Ozone is **carcinogenic**. If you ran an ozone steamer all day, you would reach the maximum daily exposure level recommended by the Health and Safety Executive. It's best not to inhale ozone, especially if you are asthmatic. If your steamer automatically adds ozone, ask your electrician if the **UV** bulb can be safely bypassed. |
| **Wet room** | If your salon has a wet area, wear non-slip, rubber-soled shoes and never run in the area. |
| **Heavy lifting** | You may be asked to move large packages of stock. While being as helpful as possible, remember that under the Manual Handling Operations Regulations 1992, you do not have to lift anything you think may be too heavy for you and may cause you damage. |
| **Eyesight** | Get your eyes checked by a high street ophthalmic optician before beginning to practise **electro-epilation**, and once a year afterwards. Eye strain will do your eyes no permanent damage but it will give you a nasty headache and your clients will prefer you to see their hair follicles clearly before you insert the probe! |
| **Pressure to work through illness** | It's fine to work through a sniffle but not through a debilitating virus such as 'flu. This will stress your body physically. You will be back to work more quickly if you rest. |

- Cuticles will bleed if over-trimmed.
- Follicles treated during **electro-epilation** sometimes leak a little **plasma** or blood.

A needle-stick injury is most risky. This is when an electrologist accidentally pierces her own skin with a used electrolysis probe. The tetanus infection can also multiply in wounds from contaminated tools.

## Take precautions against infection

Unbroken skin is the best barrier to outside infection. Cover cuts or grazes on your hands or arms with sticking plaster.

- Wear disposable latex gloves for treatments involving body fluid such as ear-piercing, **electro-epilation** and waxing. Silk glove liners are available to improve comfort and cut down on allergies.
- If you are prone to **contact dermatitis** or eczema, be especially careful to keep the skin on your hands in good condition so that it does not crack or weep.
- Use an anti-bacterial hand wash.
- Immediately swab leaking body fluid with a clean pad of cotton wool soaked in antiseptic. Dispose of this pad in a lined, lidded bin.
- Check with your doctor that your tetanus booster is up-to-date.
- Although statistics show that beauty therapists don't have a greater risk of contracting hepatitis B than the public, vaccination is still worth considering if you practise **electro-epilation**. (Ask your GP about it.)

**Figure 4.2**
Frequent hand-
washing without
moisturizing can
trigger dermatitis

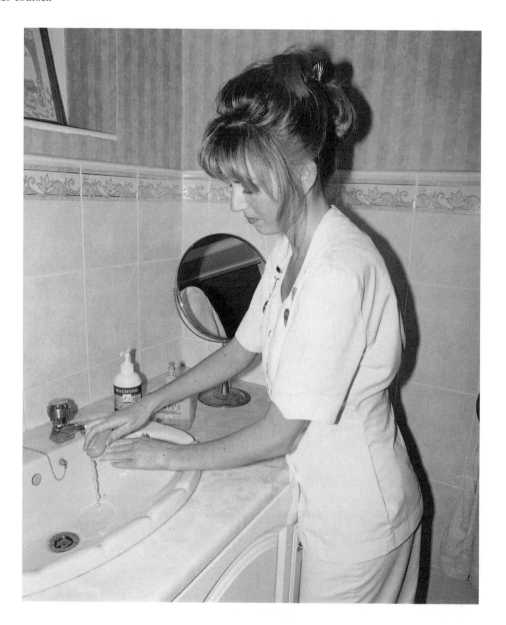

## Supportive underwear

Beauty therapy treatments can be strenuous to perform. Supportive underwear can cut down fatigue and safeguard your figure.

### Breast support

Wear a bra with adequate support. Breasts are mainly fat supported by Cooper's ligaments (which aren't true ligaments). Once over-stretched, Cooper's ligaments can never regain their shape. Have a professional bra fitting by a trained department store assistant. Sports bras are ideal since they provide comfort and avoid strap-slip.

## Leg ache

Consider wearing support tights or stockings even though you do not have varicose veins. They work by helping to pump blood back up the veins in your leg. You will be less likely to get varicose veins and leg ache will be a thing of the past.

# Physical safety

Since service industry workers work with the public, they are at slightly higher risk of attack or injury. However, beauty salons are one of the safest areas to work in and attacks are extremely rare.

## Massage and safety

The term 'massage' is sometimes used as a euphemism (a less obvious name) for sexual services. To avoid getting enquiries from men wanting sexual services, it's best to avoid using the word 'massage' when advertising. On price lists, the term 'therapeutic massage' is often used to make the difference clear.

If you run a mobile service, explain to prospective male clients that your professional working code does not allow you to visit an unchaperoned male client. If you have misgivings about a male client, trust your instincts and don't make the appointment. Only visit male clients who have been personally recommended by existing female clients.

It has been known for brothels posing as salons to recruit qualified beauty therapists to perform sexual services. (This happens mainly in large cities.) The brothels use beauty therapy qualifications to hoodwink the **Local Authority** and avoid investigation. If you are recruited to perform sexual services, report this to the police immediately. It is a criminal offence to employ prostitutes.

## Intruders

Never put yourself in danger to safeguard money or stock or sort out a disturbance. If there is a disturbance in your salon that is, or could become violent, don't confront the intruder. Phone the police immediately – from an outside phone if necessary.

# Mental wellbeing

Salon work can be mentally as well as physically stressful. Be sure to take sufficient rest and relaxation, particularly if you are self-employed. As you train you will learn the importance of:

- eating healthily
- standing and sitting well
- taking regular exercise
- getting enough sleep
- getting enough relaxation
- coping with stress.

Remember to live by what you learn, otherwise you will not be a good example to your clients.

## *Don't live your work*

The public often sees professionals as 'embodying' their profession. This means that they assume the professional image *is* the real person. As rounded individuals, most people are far more than their jobs.

While a professional image is important, remember that it is not, and should not be the whole you. If you are conscientious, it is just possible to take professionalism too far. You are not obliged to listen patiently to people's problems *outside* work. Let your hair down (literally!), dress to please yourself, express your own personality, and follow non-beauty interests.

## *Client demand*

If your ambition is to own a chain of beauty salons, don't get there by stepping on top of your friends and family. Remember that your relationship with your client is one-way. Clients buy your time; they won't be there for you when you need support, help or advice. Try to keep a healthy balance between your career and your personal life. Don't allow client-demand to rule your life. You may struggle in sick to do a wedding make-up but clients must accept that you get ill occasionally. Take time off if you are sick, take holidays, take days off, start a family if that's what you want.

## *Salon timesavers*

'Running to time' means keeping up with your booked appointment times. This can be very stressful since there are always plenty of unscheduled interruptions in a busy beauty salon. You will appear more professional if, as far as possible, you keep to your clients' appointment times. Here are a few salon time-savers that can help you catch up on time and improve service too.

- Type out **contra-indications** sheets for treatments and have them laminated by a local printer. This will save you listing **contra-indications** to each client and possibly missing one out. Of course, you must still listen to and discuss your clients' answers.
- Invite clients to fill in their own name, address and telephone number on client **record cards**. (There is less chance of a mistake this way.)
- Update your facial client's **record card** while she relaxes under her face mask.
- Replace used-up **consumables** immediately and keep cubicle supplies of cotton wool, bedroll and tissues well stocked up.
- Pump dispensers do away with removing and replacing lids – and they're more hygienic.
- Where possible, replace products that hamper you, for example, messy or hard-to-remove face masks.
- Favour time-saving preparations. For example, spray-on rather than paint-on quick-dry nail preparations.
- Where practical, combine treatments. An eyelash tint can be applied during a face mask.
- Blunt or worn equipment such as cuticle clippers slow you up – replace them.
- Blu-tack a selection of plastic nails round a plastic make-up palette. Paint the nails with your salon's selection of nail polish colours. Invite your manicure client to

select her colour while you see your last client out. Your client can also place the nail over her own to gauge the shade better. This way, she's much less likely to change her mind about the shade after you've begun applying the polish.

## Avoid addiction

Reliance on or addiction to stimulants, whether legal or illegal, is a sure sign that something is amiss in your life. This could be linked to stress, boredom, or lack of confidence. A healthy, well-balanced person doesn't need artificial stimulation or calming substances to help her enjoy or cope with life.

Drug or alcohol dependency is always incompatible with a professional lifestyle. If you need to, ask your GP for help and support as soon as possible. Everything you say will be in strict confidence.

- Tea, coffee, cola, and chocolate contain mild stimulants and are fine *in moderation*.
- Under the Workplace Health, Safety and Welfare Regulations 1992, smoking is prohibited in staff rooms unless a separate one is provided for the purpose. For this reason, as well as for reasons of health, hygiene and image, beauty therapists tend not to smoke.
- If you drink alcohol, be very careful that you don't start to depend on it to relax you after work or give you false confidence.
- Never risk a criminal record by taking illegal substances such as: marijuana (pot), recreational drugs (Ecstasy) or hard drugs (LSD, heroin or cocaine). A criminal record will make it practically impossible for you to find employment.

# Why clients confide

Sometimes clients will confide personal things to you. This confidence may be linked to treatment. Sometimes a client may confide simply because she feels relaxed and accepted.

You may wonder why she has chosen you, neither a relative nor a friend, but a professional, to confide in. There are many reasons why a client confides. She probably confided in you *because* of your professionalism. She may want to tell someone who will not judge, be shocked or upset and, most importantly, will not reject her. Generally, it isn't because she wants to develop a personal friendship with you.

## How to react when a client confides

When someone tells us a problem, we often try to suggest a solution because we want to help. Problems, particularly emotional problems, are often very complicated. The only person who can solve the problem is the person who has the problem.

When we confide, most of the time, we just want to get something off our chests; we just want someone to listen to us. When a client confides an emotional problem to you, remember that you are not a qualified counsellor and that you must not give advice. Listen without asking questions, while your client tells you about her feelings. Show that you have understood what she's told you by making an appropriate reply. It can be as simple as 'I'm *so* sorry to hear that' or 'That must have been very difficult for you.' Show sympathy. That is enough.

## How to deal with distressing disclosures

Some clients make distressing disclosures. Clients may confide, sometimes matter-of-factly, terminal illness, recent bereavement or physical or emotional abuse.

No client tells you things to upset you. She doesn't want solutions; she doesn't want to give you her pain. She wants you to know this about her, accept her and then carry on much as usual.

Generally, it's good to have **empathy** with your client (imagining how you would feel if you were her) but distressing personal disclosures are the exception. If you take on all your clients' problems throughout your working life, you will eventually cease to function. As a professional, hear what your client tells you and then let the disclosure go so that you can attend to your client's immediate treatment needs.

It's fine to make a *discreet* note of recent illness or bereavement on your client's record card. Remember to keep everything your client tells you strictly confidential. If your client tells you something very personal, never bring that subject up in conversation in later appointments unless she does so first. This could be upsetting for your client, if she isn't expecting it.

## Emotional unloading

There may be times in your life when your own problems make it difficult for you to hear your clients' problems. When this happens, listen to their words, show you have heard them but don't think about them. Simply channelling these emotions away from your client will help her enough.

---

**Remember:** When you leave your salon, leave your clients' problems there too.

---

### What do you think?

1. Your salon manager asks you to move a large conifer planted in a terracotta pot outside the salon door on opening and inside again on closing every day. You worry this will cause damage to your back. How would you explain this to your manager?

2. Your salon manager cleans the *outside* of the first floor salon windows by standing on the *outside* window ledge. One day, she asks you to clean the windows, then goes out. What do you do?

3. How can you tell if you are reliant on or addicted to a stimulant? Is there anything you could not give up?

# Chapter Five

# *Make Your Salon Inviting*

*You have chosen to work in your salon. This choice reflects on you.*

## Client comfort

Are you proud of your salon? Is it pleasant to work in? People have to visit the dentist or doctor; they don't have to visit the beauty salon. Make it an enjoyable experience, in all senses.

## Keep clients warm

The surrounding temperature in your salon is known as the **ambient temperature**. Your client will often be undressed and sitting or lying still, generating little body heat. She will feel cooler than you and cannot enjoy her treatment if she is chilly. Treatment rooms should feel comfortably warm to a therapist wearing a light overall.

If salon heating cannot be relied on, have a portable heater and extra salon blankets to hand.

## Temperature and treatments

The salon's **ambient temperature** directly affects some treatments. Incorrect temperature can mean ineffective or even painful treatment.

- Warmth is part of body massage treatment. Cold muscles cannot be effectively massaged.

- Depilatory wax cools too quickly on chilled skin. This makes it difficult to remove and more painful for your client. (See Chapter Fourteen – Something Extra, Troubleshooting: Questions and Answers.)

- Wax doesn't cool enough on over-heated skin and the same problem results. (See Chapter Fourteen – Something Extra, Troubleshooting: Questions and Answers.)

**Figure 5.1**
Ensure your client
is warm and
comfortable

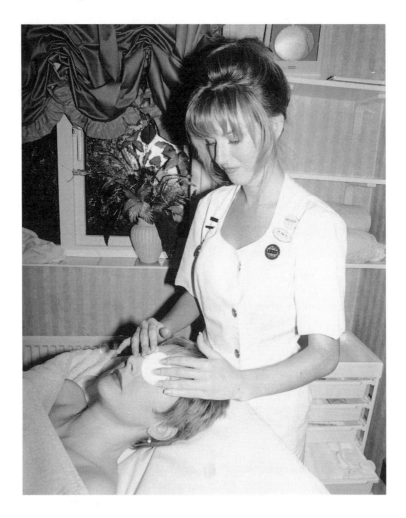

## *Ventilation*

In hot weather, salon air-conditioning is vital because steamers, saunas and sunbeds generate their own heat. If your salon isn't air-conditioned, have some electric fans to hand during summer.

Beauty cubicles, where clients dress and undress, must be well ventilated. Our sense of smell quickly fatigues, so you may not notice the unpleasant odour your client can smell on entering the cubicle. Clients will not feel comfortable in stale air. Air freshener is no substitute for fresh air.

Some salon chemicals, particularly those used during manicure, are **volatile**. For health and safety reasons, ventilation must be adequate in areas where **volatile** chemicals are used. Also, some of these chemicals have strong odours that may make some clients feel nauseous.

## *Lighting*

Salon lighting must be adequate for performing treatment effectively as well as to create a pleasant atmosphere. Many salons favour a combination of fluorescent strip-lights combined with subdued spot-lights.

**Figure 5.2**
Don't rely on
clients to tell you
if the ambient
temperature is
uncomfortable

- Ideally, apply make-up in natural daylight or under fluorescent light (choose fluorescent tubes in warm white or daylight shades).
- Lighting on salon mirrors should be level with your client's face so that it won't cast unflattering shadows across her face or give her an eerie glow!
- Use dim lighting during massage and face mask treatment. Switch to spot-lights or turn the light off.

## Sound

Beauty salons should be peaceful and relaxing. Ask clients to switch off mobile phones so that their – and others' – treatment isn't interrupted. Keep noise to a minimum. Outside noise can sometimes be a problem. Sound insulation can help:

- Fill gaps in walls and floorboards with foam filler.
- Fit doors rather than curtains to treatment rooms.
- Acoustic tiles or rubber insulation sheeting can be laid below or above floorboards to cut down noise.
- False walls can be fitted to cut down noise transmission from adjoining shops.

People are said to feel more secure and relaxed with background music. This is especially true during massage, when chatting is not appropriate. However, background music must not be intrusive. *No* music is better than annoying music.

If you decide to use background music, choose music appropriate to your salon and clientele. Some clients find modern radio stations disturbing. If staff enjoy the salon music, it is almost certainly too loud and too modern! If you don't have a **performance licence**, choose relaxation CDs that don't require one. The supplier or manufacturer can advise you on this.

## Access to a lavatory

Don't keep your lavatory a secret. Clients appreciate access to a loo! Display signs to your loo clearly but discreetly throughout your salon. For pregnant or elderly clients, just knowing a lavatory is available can make a treatment very much more comfortable.

# Keep your salon clean

If your salon doesn't look clean and tidy, your clients won't stay long enough to find out how good your treatment is.

## Temporary decorations

Don't treat temporary decorations as part of the furniture. *No* decoration is better than a shabby decoration. Ensure all displays are dust-free.

- Replace or remove silk or dried flowers and pot pourri as soon as they begin to look faded or dusty.
- Know when to say farewell to ailing, leafless plants.
- Strong sunlight quickly fades posters. 'Dog-eared and faded' is not a good salon image, particularly if displayed in the window.

## Be seen to be clean

Ask your manager's permission to check your salon for the following list of points. Always get permission for major cleaning jobs and before buying cleaning preparations. If your salon has a cleaner, are there any areas she needs to pay extra attention to? If so, recommend this to your manager.

**Table 5.1** Clean salon checklist

| Salon fitting | Cleaning tip | Checked | Needs attention |
|---|---|---|---|
| Are fluorescent light fittings free from dust and dead flies? | Carefully unclip the cover and wipe it out with detergent (washing-up liquid) on a damp cloth. | | |
| Are the floor, couch and trolley in the waxing cubicle free of wax drips and splashes? | Clean metal and vinyl surfaces with surgical spirit or specialist wax cleaner. | | |
| Are there splashes of wax on the walls? | Scrub wall or sponge vinyl wallpaper with detergent. (Cleaned walls need regular repainting. Non-vinyl wallpaper isn't suitable for waxing cubicles. Water-soluble wax is available but this can be dissolved by perspiration, which can make under-arm waxing difficult. | | |
| Can you find any dust? | Dust must be removed, not just dispersed. Wipe with a cloth dampened with spray polish. | | |
| Are air vents and extractor fans free of dust and grime? | Wipe over with a cotton wool pad dampened with surgical spirit. | | |
| Is any of the crockery cracked, chipped or stained? | Remove tannin tea stains with bicarbonate of soda (from the chemist). Replace chipped crockery. | | |

| Salon fitting | Cleaning tip | Checked | Needs attention |
|---|---|---|---|
| Are room corners free of dust and fluff? | Vacuum in corners with vacuum cleaner extension nozzle. | | |
| Are there cobwebs in any corners | Remove with long-handled duster. | | |
| Is any wallpaper peeling off at the corners? | Glue down with 'border adhesive' from a DIY store. | | |
| Are there stains on the carpet? | Remove with carpet cleaner. | | |
| Is woodwork paint chipped or peeling? | Report to manager. | | |
| Are the windows clean? | Clean with dilute detergent (washing-up liquid) and a 'squeegee' window-cleaning tool. | | |
| Are net curtains dusty or discoloured? | Wash in detergent then soak in specialist net whitening solution. | | |
| Are partition curtains or window curtains dusty or stained? | Wash or dry-clean (check label) at the launderette. | | |
| Has dust collected in wicker furniture or in louvred doors? (This type of furniture is popular because it's inexpensive, but it's unsuitable for salons because it traps dust.) | Vacuum using the brush attachment on the vacuum cleaner. | | |
| Can you find dust on top of clocks, picture frames, door frames and cupboard tops? | Wipe off with a cloth dampened with spray polish. | | |
| Are the salon nail polishes and cosmetics clean, tidy and in good order? | Wipe round tops and clean cases with tissue. | | |
| Are the salon make-up testers clean, tidy and in good order? | Wipe round tops and clean cases with tissue. | | |

## WC and wet room cleanliness

Clients will judge your standard of hygiene by the cleanliness of your wet room or lavatory. In a salon or health farm, the wet room houses the steam and water treatments. A wet room may include:

- shower
- sauna
- steam bath/cabinet
- steam room
- spa (sometimes called by the brand name Jacuzzi)
- hydrotherapy pool
- swimming pool
- plunge pool.

Clients who use wet room facilities are undressed. Unprotected by clothes, clients feel more vulnerable to grime and germs. Any hint of grime in the wet room area will make your client feel very uncomfortable.

Whether your salon has a fully fitted-out wet room, a changing area and shower cubicle or just a lavatory and wash basin, you must keep this area scrupulously clean. Have different coloured rubber gloves for the crockery and the lavatory – and label them accordingly!

**Table 5.2** Wet room checklist

| Wet room facility | Cleaning tip | Checked | Needs attention |
|---|---|---|---|
| Is the lavatory brush clean and in good condition? | Rinse thoroughly under a running tap with detergent, then soak in a bucket of dilute bleach. | | |
| Are wastes to showers and basins free from hair and gunge? | Clean out with an old toothbrush kept for the purpose. | | |
| Is there a growth of mould on the shower curtain? | Machine wash on 60°C. | | |
| Is there mould anywhere – for example, on shower seats? | Wipe or scrub with detergent. | | |
| Is the water supply to the showers and the spa pool filtration system properly maintained? | **Pathogens** such as legionella can quickly multiply in filters and faulty showers. The infectious microbes are then inhaled in water splashes. | | |

## Limescale

If your wet room equipment, tiling and sanitary fittings – lavatory and basin – look dull and lifeless; you're suffering from **limescale**. Fortunately, it's quite curable. It is not enough to hose down these areas daily with detergent. Deposits in the water – especially in hard water areas – build up as **limescale** on tiled and ceramic surfaces. (It's the same substance that 'furs up' kettles.) **Limescale** build-up looks and feels like fine grey-white cement. It's unsightly and harbours germs. Clean it off regularly with a specialist cleaning product. On *ceramic* tiles and enamel, e.g. the lavatory, you can clean it off effectively with a pumice stone – not the salon one!

Areas where limescale collects are:

■ round the rim and in the U-bend of the lavatory bowl
■ around sanitary fittings such as taps. (Apply limescale remover with a toothbrush reserved for the purpose.)

## Drains

Blocked drains smell bad and can spread disease. Bottle or tubular traps are fitted below all hand basins and sinks. They act as water seals, designed to prevent drain contents and odours from travelling back up the waste pipe and ending up in the basin. If your basin smells bad or water drains slowly, the trap may be blocked.

- Unscrew and scrub the trap occasionally to ensure that it is clear. Remember to place a bucket under the trap when you do this!

- Don't block the trap by pouring surplus cosmetics such as clay face masks down the basin drain. Put them in the waste bin.

- A solution of caustic soda (sodium hydroxide) can be used to clear pipes and drains blocked further along. Follow the instructions on the bottle very carefully. Caustic soda is a very hazardous chemical.

- Sanitary towels and tampons can quickly block lavatory pipes and drains. It pays to provide sanitary disposal bins in the lavatory. If you don't have the bins collected by a specialist company, contact your **Local Authority** to find out how to dispose of the contents.

## Be prepared

A 'contingency' is something that may happen. It could be a slight inconvenience such as laddering your tights or it could be a major event that interests the media. Whether you are a trainee or manager of a large health hydro, don't wait until something goes wrong, think ahead and plan how best to get round salon snarl-ups. Make sure all staff know the contingency plans for occurrences such as:

- injury or accident to staff or clients
- a fire
- a gas leak
- a flood
- a bomb alert
- electrical equipment failure
- a power cut
- a water supply cut
- an intruder.

### What do you think?

1. Cellular blankets – blankets with holes – are a popular choice for salons. They look attractive and are designed to be light but also trap body-heat. What is the best way to stop your client's body-heat escaping through the holes in cold weather?

2. How does your salon look from a client's-eye view? Lie on the treatment couch. What can you see? An assortment of flies building up in the fluorescent light fitting?

# Chapter Six

# Look Professional

*The more professional you look, the more confident you will feel.*

## The importance of appearance

You are a walking advertisement for yourself and your salon. The more professional you look, the more confidence your clients will have in you and your salon. And this is even before you begin treatment.

You have chosen to work in the beauty industry. No doubt, you are interested in cosmetics. Put into practice everything you learn as you train. Your skill will reflect in your figure, hands and face. This doesn't mean that all successful therapists are slim with flawless complexions. Like women in general, therapists come in all skin-types, shapes and sizes. Indeed, many women feel more comfortable with a less-than-perfect therapist.

**Figure 6.1** How we judge people

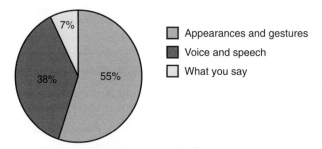

- Appearances and gestures
- Voice and speech
- What you say

7%
38%
55%

## Be nice to be near

You will be working in close contact with your clients. Personal freshness is vital. Be sure to have a bath or shower every morning. This is particularly important in warm weather.

### Body odour

Use an effective combined antiperspirant and deodorant. Antiperspirant reduces perspiration. Deodorant reduces the bacterial breakdown of sweat, which gives the unpleasant under-arm body odour known as BO. Antiperspirant deodorants work best if applied to hair-free skin and allowed to dry before you dress. Keep a spare antiperspirant deodorant at work for the day when you forget to wear it!

## Perfume

Perfume or body spray will not mask body odour. If you wear perfume, be sure it is very light. Your client could easily feel stifled by a heavy scent. Some clients have allergies to strong fragrances.

## Fresh breath

You will be breathing over your clients.

- Be sure to clean your teeth every morning and after lunch if you have time. Keep a toothbrush and toothpaste at work.
- Use antiseptic mouthwash if you need to.
- Once gum disease sets in, it's difficult to cure. Floss your teeth regularly and visit your dentist every six months so that your teeth stay healthy. Decay in cavities and unhealthy gums gives off that unpleasant 'bad breath' odour called halitosis.
- Your clients won't enjoy the smell of spicy food or garlic on your breath. Restrict such foods to when you're not working.
- Stale cigarette smoke is equally unpleasant.

## Hair care

Keep your hair clean, in good condition and attractively styled.

- Use an effective dandruff shampoo if you need to.
- It makes sense to choose a hairstyle that is easy to maintain.
- Make sure long hair is tied back or pinned up so that when you lean over your client, your hair doesn't touch her or dangle in any of the preparations.
- Remember that some mid-length styles can be difficult to tie back neatly.

## Skin care and make-up

Keep your skin in good condition and don't pile on too much make-up.

- A light make-up is easier to keep up every day.
- Some clients feel intimidated by heavily made-up therapists and assume they will leave looking the same way.

## Hands

Just like your face, your hands are an advert for your profession. Put into practice the theory you learn about hand and nail care. Keep your hands in good condition and be aware of salon hazards to healthy skin.

**Figure 6.2**
Maintain a
professional
appearance

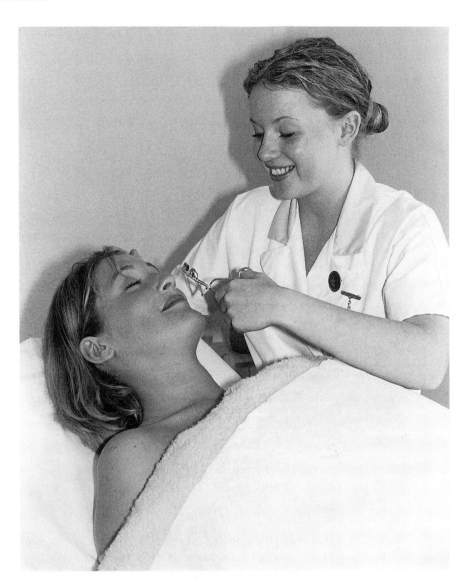

- In the salon, frequent hand-washing is necessary for hygiene but removes natural oils and quickly dries out skin.

- Some salon preparations, such as nail polish remover and surgical spirit, have a drying effect and can irritate sensitive skin.

- Activated eyelash tint will stain any skin it comes into contact with including your fingers and nails! You will fail a tinting assessment if you allow tint to stain your own fingers. If you are a messy tinter, wear disposable gloves.

- Self-tanning cream will stain skin as well as fabric. Keep it away from clothing. Thoroughly wash the cream off your hands and scrub your nails as soon as you finish treatment.

- Regularly inspect your hands for **verrucae**. The **verruca** virus is contagious, especially on moist skin. On hands, a **verruca** infection is commonly called a wart.

- Don't wait to develop **contact dermatitis**. Apply hand cream regularly during the day – keep a pump dispenser by the hand basin – and last thing at night. **Contact dermatitis** is not **contagious** but looks unsightly and can seriously affect your career if it becomes chronic and you cannot work.

At the first sign of any skin disorder on your hands or nails, particularly **contact dermatitis**, visit your GP and explain that not only must your hands be healthy, they must look healthy.

> **Did you know?** The odour from chopped onions and garlic lingers on hands for several hours, even days! Avoid this by wearing latex rubber gloves at home when chopping onions and garlic.

## Nails

Your fingernails must be and look healthy. They should be:

- Clean; keep a nail brush by the hand basin.
- Short but not bitten. Long nails harbour germs and however skilful you are, you can't avoid scratching your client during **electro-epilation** or massage.
- Unpolished. Nail polish cracks as it wears. The cracks harbour germs. This is equally true of clear polish.
- Neither you nor your client can see if your nails are clean through polish.
- Some clients are allergic to pigments such as eosins used in nail polish.

It's fine for salon workers who don't have much physical contact with clients, such as receptionists, fitness instructors and manicurists to wear nail polish. If nail polish is worn, it should not be smudged or chipped.

> **Did you know?** A professional manicurist must be able to remove and apply clients' nail polish without smudging her own. Hold the cotton wool pad in the crook of your fingers, a third of the way down from the tips, away from your own nails.

# Clothing and accessories

## Uniforms

Most salons have a staff uniform such as an overall or a tunic and trousers. Uniforms are generally white but they can be a pastel shade. Your outfit may be more casual, depending on your salon's image. You'll need at least two uniforms: one to wear and one to wash. Your employer may provide your uniforms or you may buy them yourself.

Look after your uniforms carefully – they reflect your professional image. If you worked in an office and your blouse became stained with red and black ink, you wouldn't carry on wearing it, would you? A uniform stained with black eyelash tint and red nail polish looks equally unprofessional. Replace it, even if you have to pay for a new one yourself.

- Regularly wash and iron your uniforms.

> **Did you know?** To prevent polycotton uniforms becoming shiny, iron them on the wrong side.

- Take particular care to protect your uniform from nail polish spills, wax splashes and eyelash tint. If need be, wear a plastic apron when using these products.
- Replace lost buttons and sew up lose hems or split seams as soon as you spot them.
- When you are outside the salon, protect your uniform by covering it with a full-length coat or mac.
- Wear a slip or half-slip under your uniform so that your underwear isn't easily visible, particularly when standing against the light.
- For a fully groomed look, it's considered professional always to wear stockings or tights with your uniform. You can get away with 'knee-highs' if your uniform is long enough.

> **Remember:** The secret to a professional appearance is being well prepared. Keep a spare uniform – perhaps an old one – and a spare pair of tights at your salon. One day you'll be glad you did.

### Jewellery

A fob watch, pinned to your uniform, is a good alternative to a wristwatch and looks professional. As a trainee or qualified therapist, join a professional association such as **BABTAC** and wear your member's badge on your uniform. Your client can then see that you belong to a professional body.

**Figure 6.3**
A fob watch

- Wear only a wedding ring on your hands. Other jewellery on your figures or wrists can scratch or tickle your client.

- Rings, bracelets and watches can harbour germs.

- Other jewellery such as earrings and necklaces should be discreet and never dangle over your client.

## Foot wear

Leather shoes have an advantage over plastic ones. Leather allows air flow to and from the foot, reducing the chances of foot odour. If necessary, use deodorizing inner soles or foot spray.

Salon footwear is low-heeled and usually white but check with your employer. Closed-in shoes are preferable since they protect your feet from wax drips. Your shoes must be in good condition. White shoes wear more quickly than darker colours. White shoe polish can improve their appearance until you need to replace them.

You will be spending quite a bit of time on your feet. Buy the best quality shoes you can afford. Consider cushioned soles to cut down on impact to your knee joints.

# Mobile and home-based therapists

A professional image is especially important for a mobile therapist. Your appearance is all your client has to judge your professionalism.

Home-based therapists should be particularly careful to keep up professional standards. For example, assume clients don't want to bump into children and pets unless they tell you otherwise.

# Look the part

## First impressions

You never get a second chance to make a first impression. Your client's first impression will affect her overall opinion of your treatment. If a therapist appears professional and confident, clients may mistake mediocre treatment for good treatment. This is because, subconsciously, people don't like to reverse their first impressions. Of course, this is not an excuse for poor treatment, but it shows how strong first impressions are. Likewise, it's likely that clients will be surprised and even puzzled to find a sloppy-looking therapist giving expert treatment.

## Stereotypes

Clients feel happiest when professionals conform to a stereotype. A stereotype is a standardized mental picture. For example, an old man with tousled hair, a monocle and a bow tie is more likely to be picked out as a professor than a fashionably dressed young women because his image fits our stereotype better. Close your eyes and think of a beauty therapist. What did you see? The chances are, she didn't have purple hair or a pierced eyebrow. If you conform to the beauty therapist stereotype, this will reinforce your professional image.

Be as unconventional as you like outside work but try not to allow your personal image to compromise your professional one. If you yearn for a tattoo, make sure it's hidden by your uniform. If you feel the urge to express yourself through body piercing, take the sleepers or studs out for work.

> **Remember:** You can't sound – or look – professional while chewing gum.

## Age

It's a plus if beauty therapists look younger than their years but at the beginning of your career, this can work against you. Once your clients get to know you, they will respect your expertise and in time, your experience. But until then, you can appear more experienced by:

■ wearing well-applied make-up

■ wearing your hair up

■ acting confidently

■ speaking maturely.

## Tools and equipment that enhance professionalism

It's not enough to be professional. *Be seen* to be professional. Using professional equipment will make your treatment more effective than anything your client can do for herself at home:

■ Use a professional stainless steel **comedone** extractor to remove **comedones** and **milia**. Experiment with the standard and loop-end design to see which one you prefer.

**Figure 6.4**
Four different kinds of comedone extractor

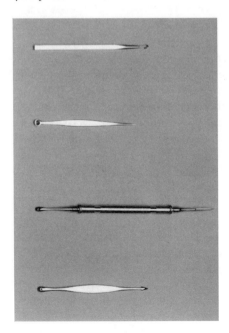

- Always use a magnifying lamp when performing skin analysis and **electro-epilation**. Working with a lamp may seem fiddly at first but magnification greatly improves accuracy and also prevents eye strain.

- Use specialized **electro-epilation** forceps for **electro-epilation**. These are different from regular tweezers. If the grip is loose on fine hair, improve the contact by smoothing over the points with fine emery paper.

- Try **automatic tweezers**, many clients prefer these.

- Use eyelash curlers before applying eye make-up.

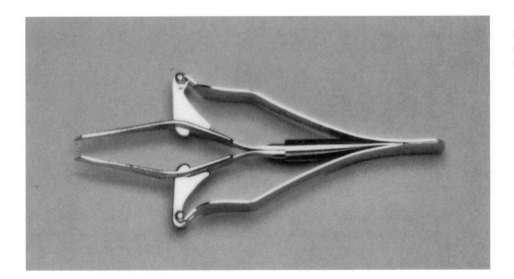

**Figure 6.5**
Spring-loaded automatic tweezers

- Use a professional leather nail buffer and buffing cream during manicure.

- Set a timer with a buzzer – a digital egg timer is ideal – for treatments with specific development times, such as lash tinting. When the buzzer sounds, your client will be reassured that she's had the correct length of treatment time. Ensure the buzzer doesn't disturb your client during relaxing treatments.

- Use fabric strips for waxing treatment. Bonded paper strips are false economy since more strips are needed to remove the same amount of wax. Paper strips also tear easily. This could make you appear less competent.

## What do you think?

1. A therapist likes to wear her nails long, so she performs massage using her knuckles rather than her fingers. What do you think about her professionalism?

2. You have a colleague who regularly has to rush out of the salon to stand outside, by the dustbins, for five minutes, sometimes in the rain. When she comes back, she has to brush her teeth and gargle with mouthwash. She also has to wash her hair and uniform every evening and soak her fingers in peroxide once a week. Why do you think she has so much extra trouble?

# Chapter Seven

# *Act Professionally*

*Begin your training professionally and stay professional throughout your career.*

## Behave professionally with clients

You will be performing treatments – some intimate treatments – on about a dozen people every working day. At the beginning of your career, these people will be strangers. Some of them will be nervous. To make them feel as relaxed as possible, it is important that you develop a confident manner when dealing with people you don't know.

The way you behave will have a big effect on every treatment you perform. Your client will pick up information from the things you say, your facial expressions and your mannerisms. How do you greet a stranger? Is your greeting confident? Practise with a colleague.

- Smile.
- Greet your client by name if possible.
- Tell your client your name.
- Invite her to follow you to the treatment room.

As you speak to your client:

- Make good eye contact – but don't stare at her so that she feels uncomfortable.
- Keep an open and relaxed body posture: avoid crossing your arms or standing with hand on hip.
- Appear calm and relaxed, even if you have been rushed off your feet.
- Avoid staring or showing distaste at any physical **anomaly** your client may have.

### Develop client rapport

A rapport (t is silent) is a harmonious relationship. If you create a rapport with your client, she will feel relaxed in your company. Many different types of people visit beauty salons. Try to find a rapport with all your clients. A rapport will come naturally with some clients, with others you will have to work harder at developing it. As your client talks to you, notice which topics interest her and see if you can find something in common to chat about. (See Chapter Eight – Sound Professional.)

## When to be assertive

To assert means 'to state clearly'. To be assertive is to state clearly what you want to happen. Don't confuse assertiveness with aggressiveness. Aggressive people get their way by bullying. Aggression has no place in a professionally run salon.

You may need to be assertive to safeguard your client's health, discourage her from unsuitable treatment or ensure professional results from treatment. For example:

- Refuse to allow your client to use the sunbed when she has developed any of the following symptoms due to sunbathing: **erythema**, peeling, swelling or blistering.
- Don't be persuaded to perform treatment that, in your judgement, is unsuitable. For example, don't apply black eyebrows with **micropigmentation** on a blonde client.
- If appropriate, ask your client to book a course of treatment rather than odd sessions of, for example, mechanical massage or **electro-epilation**.

## Keeping client confidentiality

Clients may discuss their finances and friendships with you or tell you personal details. Under the Data Protection Act 1998 information confided to you or recorded on a **client record card** or on a computer database must never be repeated to anyone, passed on in any form or copied. This rule is especially important for celebrity clients. *Nothing* will persuade a true professional to reveal any client information to anyone.

The Data Protection Act 1998 requires anyone who holds personal details on computer to be registered with the Data Protection Registrar (see *Useful Addresses*). This law is currently being extended to cover manually written records also. If you are disposing of a salon computer, wipe or destroy the hard disk to protect your clients' personal details.

## Don't give selective discounts

Don't offer reduced prices to certain clients, such as long-term **electro-epilation** clients, unless they pre-pay for a course. Varying prices will cause bad feeling among other clients. It's better to 'gift' treatment. This means that if you have a few extra minutes to spare, offer to continue the treatment for a little longer. Be sure to ask first; some clients can't tolerate a longer session of **electro-epilation**!

## Receiving tips and gratuities

In service industries, some customers leave extra money as a gratuity or tip. Traditionally, this is 10 per cent of the cost of the service. Legally, all tips are classed as 'earned income' and are taxable. Customers may tip because service industry wages are not high or because they are pleased with the service. Some industries put their tips together and share them out equally but this is not common in beauty salons. Some clients feel embarrassed about tipping. Some do not believe in tipping.

Your client may:

- Hand you a tip as you finish her treatment.
- Hand you a tip as she pays for treatment.
- Ask you for change so that she can tip you.
- Invite you to keep the change from treatment.
- Leave a tip for you at reception. (Some salon receptions have discreet boxes so money is not left lying around.)
- Leave a tip in the beauty room or on the treatment trolley.
- Tip only at Christmas.
- Tip before manicure treatment because she doesn't want to smudge her nail polish after treatment.
- Tip before treatment because she hopes to encourage you to do a good job.
- Add your tip onto her cheque or credit card bill. (Take your tip in change from the till to save your employer having to add it onto your salary at the end of the month.)

Of course, getting a tip will make no difference to the quality of your service which, as a professional, is always the best you can provide. You may offend your client if you refuse her tip so, unless you feel strongly about it, accept tips graciously but discreetly with a simple 'Thank you'. If it's an impressive tip, you can add 'very much'.

## Act professionally during treatment

### Consultations

In beauty therapy, traditionally no charge is made for a **consultation**. This means that a prospective or existing client may book a **consultation** to discuss any beauty matter free of charge, without being obliged to book treatment. In practice, most clients do book treatments. A **consultation** should be:

- free of charge
- held in private
- 10–15 minutes long
- confidential
- include a patch test for allergies if appropriate.

### Watching treatment

Behave professionally if you are given the opportunity to watch a colleague treat a client.

### Dos and don'ts while watching treatment:

- Remember, you are not invisible. Smile and say hello to your colleague's client.
- Don't make your colleague's client feel uncomfortable by staring at her or inspecting the condition of her nail polish as your colleague talks to her.
- It's generally more interesting to do than to watch – but don't look bored or fidget.
- Your colleague may explain the treatment to you at appropriate moments. Don't interrupt at other times. Save your questions until after the client leaves.
- Thank the client for allowing you to watch her treatment.

Even when you are qualified, never turn down the opportunity to watch another therapist work or experience a treatment; you may learn something that improves your own technique.

### Don't interrupt treatment

Once you have started treatment, it's unprofessional to allow interruptions from staff or to leave your client until treatment is complete. (Politely explain this, if need be, to colleagues and trainees.) Once you begin a massage, you should not lose contact with your client's skin throughout the treatment.

- Prepare all equipment and tools before treatment begins.
- Don't leave treatment to attend to your previous client, for example if she has smudged her nail polish. Suggest instead that a competent receptionist or trainee help.

## Be seen to be professional

It is not enough for clients to *believe* you are professional; they must *see* you are professional. Make a habit of following hygienic practices in view of your client. Here are some procedures clients can see you doing:

- Washing your hands before treatment.
- Opening a sealed **electro-epilation** probe – scrunch up the packet as you put it in the bin, if you like!
- Selecting a new waxing spatula.
- Changing the bedroll.
- Taking equipment from the sterilizer or sterilizing fluid.
- Transferring creams or cosmetics with a spatula.
- Applying cosmetics from a pallet.

Of course, you don't have to make these practices obvious or mention them to your client unless she asks about them. You can then explain that it is to prevent **cross-infection**.

## Keep your eyes on your client

You will need to keep your thoughts and eyes focused on your client when you perform most treatments. Continue to keep your eyes focused on the area you are working on, even when it is not strictly necessary, for example during massage.

## The importance of touch

Comfortable physical contact between you and your client is an important aspect of treatment. Develop a firm, confident touch. This is especially useful during pedicure; feet can be particularly ticklish. Clients may not realize it but physical contact is an aspect of beauty treatment most people find particularly soothing. Where possible, make some physical contact during electrical treatments such as mechanical massage. For example, keep one hand in contact with your client's skin as you work with the equipment.

## Maintain professional confidence

If you need to correct a mistake during treatment, such as when applying make-up, hurriedly wiping off several wrong shades will look unprofessional and irritate your client's skin. Correct mistakes so that your client doesn't lose confidence in your professional ability. Here are some techniques for correcting unsuitable make-up:

- Gently blend away unsuitable eye-shadow with foundation applied to a cosmetic sponge. Brush over with little loose powder on a fluff brush.
- Press firmly over unsuitable lipstick with a folded tissue. If necessary, work some petroleum jelly over the lip area with a lip brush, and then re-blot with tissue.
- Remove unsuitable eyeliner by working over with a little foundation applied to a clean eyeliner brush. Blend away eyeliner residue with the edge of a cosmetic sponge.
- Remove unsuitable blusher by pressing over liberally with loose powder and brushing it off with a clean blusher brush.

## Use professional-looking equipment and techniques

Even when it makes no difference to the effectiveness of the treatment, it's still important to keep up your professional image.

- Don't slip into the habit of using your finger nail rather than a cotton wool-tipped orange wood stick to push back cuticles or remove nail polish from a flooded cuticle. This manicurist's short-cut may save a little time but remember that it looks unprofessional to both examiners and clients.

**Figure 7.1**
A professional
foot spa

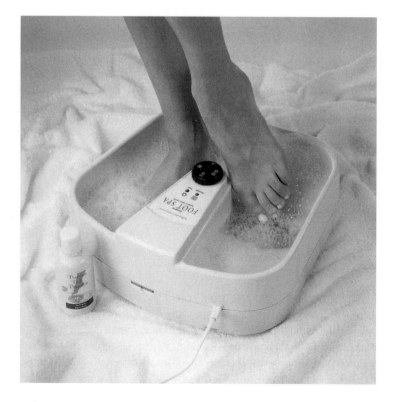

- Replace bedding, gowns or towels that have become stained with wax, nail polish or eyelash tint. They may be freshly laundered but they won't look clean.
- During manicure and pedicure, soak your clients' hands and feet in professional-looking receptacles such as a non-spill manicure bowl and a foot spa – rather than a pudding basin and washing-up bowl.
- Use professional-looking clinic or digital scales for weighing clients, not bathroom scales.

## Handling complaints professionally

It's never easy to receive a complaint or hear criticism, especially when you've been trying hard to give a good service. Can you hear a complaint calmly and think about it without getting upset? This is a skill you can learn. It's well worth learning too. It's much easier for a client to complain to a defensive, aggressive or rude service-provider because there is no 'relationship' to make the complainer feel mean.

Getting a complaint gives you the chance to show just how professional you are. Telling you about a shortcoming is your client's way of showing she cares about your service and products and values you as a professional. Think of complaints as useful, learn to value them and turn them to your advantage. They can help you and your salon stay professional.

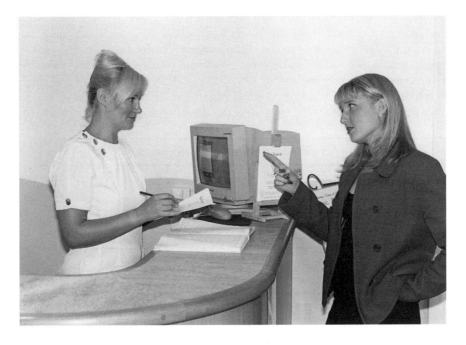

**Figure 7.2**
An angry client who has mistaken her appointment time

### Listen to the complaint

If your client makes a complaint:

- Show her to a quiet part of the salon, sit down with her, maybe offer some refreshment and give her a few minutes' undivided attention.
- Begin by thanking your client for taking the time and trouble to tell you of the matter.

- Invite her to explain the problem. Let her do this without interruption and listen to what she says.

- Remember to stay calm while your client explains her complaint. This may mean making a conscious effort to relax. Keep an 'open' body posture; don't cross your arms or legs.

- Once your client has finished, repeat back to her what she's told you to show you have listened and understood.

Your client will be feeling much more positive about the situation, and you haven't even offered a solution yet. Well done!

> **Remember:**   When dealing with a complaining client:
>
> ■ Never argue.
>
> ■ Never allow fear to make you appear defensive or aggressive.
>
> ■ Never allow nervousness to make you appear amused.

## Product complaints

If your client simply doesn't like your product you don't have to refund her money, but why not offer an exchange or refund? Your salon may like to consider adopting the policy of offering a full refund against any product that the client does not like. This makes products much easier to sell and shows how much your salon cares about clients' satisfaction.

Returns are generally few and are soon outweighed by increased sales and good customer relations. Of course, returned products can't be resold but when there is no danger of **cross-infection**, they can be used up in the salon or put out as testers.

**Figure 7.3**
Dealing with a complaint about faulty goods

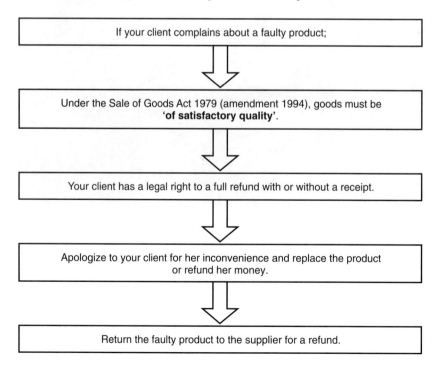

| If your client complains about a faulty product; |
| --- |

| Under the Sale of Goods Act 1979 (amendment 1994), goods must be **'of satisfactory quality'**. |
| --- |

| Your client has a legal right to a full refund with or without a receipt. |
| --- |

| Apologize to your client for her inconvenience and replace the product or refund her money. |
| --- |

| Return the faulty product to the supplier for a refund. |
| --- |

## Service complaints

If your client complains about a treatment that was not at fault, she has probably misunderstood what the treatment could do. Show concern that she is disappointed and explain more fully about the treatment, taking care not to make your client feel foolish. One way of avoiding complaints like this is to be honest about what treatments can and can't do. If you suspect the treatment will not satisfy your client, explain to her fully why you feel this before agreeing to do the treatment.

If the complaint is a minor dispute over something like a small price discrepancy, it's usually best to keep your client happy. But make sure she's put right for next time.

If you made a mistake, apologize, offer to put the situation right at once and make no charge or offer a full refund. Do all you can to make your client happy. Most will be pleased and relieved to accept.

Lastly, record the complaint details and your action on your client's **record card** in case she takes the complaint further.

# Work professionally

## Develop initiative

Using your initiative means being able to get on with your work without being prompted by others. This is a very valued skill in the beauty salon. Taking the initiative is a skill that improves with practice.

When you first begin work in your salon, start by watching how things are done. You may notice that something which is usually done has not been done. In the case of a straightforward task like washing-up, you can go ahead and do it. You may notice, for example, that a waxing appointment is booked but the waxer has not been switched on, or the waxer needs cleaning or the lining paper on the manicure trolley needs changing. If you aren't sure whether you should do something, always ask first.

Beauty treatment is seasonal. This means that certain times of year are less busy. A quiet spell can be a welcome rest if the previous season has been very busy. No-one will object to you having the odd tea-break if business is very slack, or your top-to-toe client doesn't turn up. However the chances are your employer will prefer to see you busy yourself with some useful task rather than sit at reception reading a novel. There's always something to do in a salon. Seasonal lulls are useful for spring-cleaning or reorganizing the salon.

## Develop a conscientious approach to work

Being conscientious means taking your responsibilities seriously. In the salon, this means getting everything done that needs doing and making sure you do everything you say you will.

It's important that accurate treatment records are kept on client **record cards**. In a busy salon it is sometimes hard to find time to fill them in but be sure to do this. Accurate records help you give your clients the best service. And you may need to refer to them if your client has a query or complaint about treatment.

## Be reliable

Your clients and your colleagues will depend on you to fulfil your role in the salon. If you fail to do this, you will disappoint your clients and your colleagues will have to cover for you. If you make a habit of being unreliable, you will soon be considered unprofessional.

Your tutor or salon manager will not expect you to struggle in if you are too ill to work. Sometimes, illness comes on suddenly, but don't leave it to the last minute to phone in sick. Tell your salon manager as soon as you realize you will be too ill to work. She needs as much time as possible to arrange for a colleague to cover your work or cancel your clients. Keep your manager updated about your illness. It's also helpful if you can give your manager an idea of when you will be fit for work again.

## Be a good time-keeper

In a salon, it is particularly important to arrive at work in good time. Allow enough time for travelling plus delays. Aim to arrive at work 15 minutes before your first appointment so that you have time to prepare for it. If you have a waxing appointment at 9 a.m., you will need to arrive at work at 8.45 to heat the wax.

Arriving early for work has an advantage for you. You will start the working day off well and your appointments will be less likely to run late. It's professional – though not always easy – to keep to your clients' appointment times. This will keep clients happy and encourage them to arrive on time since you do not keep them waiting. If you work in a large complex such as a health farm, ensure that your clients understand the importance of arriving on time for their treatment appointments. If need be, go and fetch them.

Why is it important to run to time? When clients book treatment during their lunch hours, for instance, they need to get back to work on time, just like you. If you become delayed during an appointment, let your receptionist know so that she can tell your next client there is a short delay.

> **Remember:** If you find it difficult, initially, to fit treatment into its allotted time, set yourself mini time limits for each stage of treatment. For example, allow three minutes for preparing your client, four minutes for deep cleansing and so on. You'll soon develop a working routine and won't need to check your watch so often.

Devote an appropriate length of time to each treatment. This is important for running a cost-effective salon. A treatment such as a manicure can take up a lot of time for a small charge. It is fairer to clients as well as better for your salon to devote most time to the more costly treatments.

## Plan treatments effectively

When a client books several treatments, plan them logically, particularly when manicure is included. It is often helpful to paint nails early on in treatment so that they have time to dry before the client leaves. But remember that your client will not be able to undress with wet nails. For example, if your client books a leg wax and manicure, ask her to change into a dressing robe, then paint her nails. These can be drying while you wax her legs. Here are some examples of treatment planning:

- Manicure and pedicure treatment can be combined. Soak your client's feet while you file her nails. Alternate painting toenails and fingernails, allowing each to dry. Finish toenails first because shoes smudge tacky polish.
- An eyelash tint can be incorporated into a facial, during the face mask.

■ Various treatments can be combined with electronic muscle exercisers. In fact, this is the best way to make such equipment cost-effective because treatment time is lengthy compared to cost.

## Be organized

Think ahead. It's unprofessional to interrupt another therapist's treatment because you need a tool or piece of equipment in her room. Take out what you need before treatment begins.

Incorporate tidiness into your work routines. Tidy working means safer working. Open jars, wax drips, trailing cables and stock or equipment left lying about may cause a hazard to you, your colleagues or clients. A tidy worker also looks more professional.

Try to avoid leaving a messy treatment room for a colleague to tidy, though sometimes this can't be avoided. Some 'tidiness' only comes with practice. As you get more experienced at waxing you will drip less wax!

# Develop a professional manner

## Have a sense of responsibility

Being responsible means behaving in a way you know to be right. As a beauty therapist, you must guard against any action that may harm you, your client or your colleagues.

Give an excellent service but also work cost-effectively. Use salon equipment and **consumable goods** responsibly and don't waste them. Treat salon equipment like your own. A cost-effective salon benefits its staff as well as its owners.

## Be trustworthy and honest

The public puts professionals in 'a position of trust'. People are more shocked when a professional is found guilty of **misconduct**. Your colleagues and clients will trust you as a professional. This means you will automatically be trusted with:

■ salon money
■ salon stock
■ keeping clients' details confidential
■ taking care of clients' valuables.

Any breach of trust is gross **misconduct** which can result in instant dismissal without a reference.

> **Remember:** Suggest to a client who leaves her watch or jewellery in the treatment room or on the manicure trolleys, that she should put valuables into her purse. This is the best way to ensure no jewellery is ever mislaid or forgotten.

Any claim you make about a product or service must stand up to the scrutiny of the Trading Standards Association. This doesn't just apply to what's on the product box. It includes how you describe your treatment in words and writing. Is your microcurrent facial treatment *really* as effective as a face-lift or just the next best thing? Can your lash tint *really* make lashes longer, or just appear longer?

Your goods must also be 'fit for their purpose'. If you tell your client a mascara is waterproof and it isn't, you will be contravening the Trades Descriptions Act of 1968 and 1972 or the Misrepresentation Act 1967.

## Be tactful

Having tact means treating other people's feelings sensitively. A useful way to check whether your comments to a client are tactful is to imagine yourself as that client, then imagine how you would feel if someone made the comment to you.

Imagine you decide to have your legs waxed for the first time. You stop shaving them for a month. At the salon you say to your beauty therapist, 'I feel embarrassed my legs are so hairy.' How would you feel if she said, 'So they are! I've never seen legs quite that hairy before!' If you tell your client that her body hair is natural and normal, she'll be grateful for your reassurance – but it's highly unlikely she'll then decide to keep it!

Being tactful sometimes means holding back on the truth to spare your client's feelings. If your client has an unsightly feature, such as severe cellulite, you can be sure that she's already well aware of it. She doesn't need you to spell it out in the hope of selling a course of treatment. After all, you are in the business of making clients feel good as well as look good.

Clients sometimes ask ill-informed questions or make groundless complaints. When this happens, it's easy to make your client look or feel foolish. For example, clients often ask whether the price for leg waxing is for one or both legs. Always listen carefully to such questions or complaints and give a serious answer. Save your giggles until after your client has left.

## Behave with discretion

Being discreet means being careful not to embarrass your client. Different things embarrass different people. Avoid doing or saying anything that could possibly embarrass your client.

Being discreet means not mentioning certain treatments loudly. Some **electro-epilation** or waxing clients may feel embarrassed if you announce their treatment to a group of waiting clients.

> **Remember:** Out of sight doesn't necessarily mean out of earshot. Wall partitions, noise from salon equipment, and curtains don't necessary stop sound carrying.

Anything you find out about your client must be kept strictly confidential. This applies to everything your client tells you and anything you notice about her. Never discuss one client with another client even if you do not mention her by name. If you break this rule two things will happen:

- The first client's trust is betrayed.
- The second client will be afraid you will tell someone about *her*.

If you're not sure about the relationship of people who arrive with your client, always assume the relationship that is least likely to embarrass your client. Assume:

- children are children rather than grandchildren
- a man is a husband rather than a son
- a woman is a friend rather than a daughter.

## Boost your client's confidence

Confidence in our looks is mostly in our heads. You don't believe me? Think back to the last time you wore a fantastic new outfit. You looked forward to wearing it and felt great, didn't you? When you wore the outfit the second time, it didn't feel the same, did it? Nothing had changed, except *your* perception of how you looked.

People develop self-confidence at different stages in life. Children with a loving and supportive home-life develop it early. Hopefully, it develops further in teen years. Some older people are still searching for it. This can be true of women who have brought up families rather than followed a career. A beauty treatment can give a big boost to self-confidence. It can help a woman say: *'Now I'm ready to do what I need to do.'*

Don't hold back on complimenting your clients. A genuine compliment is always welcome. It also shows that your attention is fixed on your client. Make a nervous, shy or uncertain client feel more at ease by complimenting her on some aspect of the appearance early on in the **consultation**.

### What do you think?

1. A regular client phones to ask for a colleague's address. The client wants to send the colleague a Christmas card. What do you do?

2. There do exist 'habitual complainers' who make a habit or even a profession of complaining and gaining free treatment or compensation money. For example, people who knowingly have an allergy to **toluenediamine** dye have treatment at salons which don't carry out **patch tests**, then sue. How would you avoid this happening to you?

# Chapter Eight

# Sound Professional

*Speech is a primary means of communication.*

## Telephone technique

Your telephone client cannot see your professionalism: make sure she hears it. It's important to smile on the phone! The 'smile' will come through in your voice. In the same way, irritation or impatience can also be heard in your voice.

Speak clearly and slowly. Your salon may have a set greeting or it may be up to you how you greet your caller.

- Tell your caller the name of your salon.
- Give your name.
- Ask how you may help her.

> **Remember:** The more polite you are on the phone, the more professional you will sound. Sounding professional over the phone is particularly important if you work from home or run a mobile service.

## May I?

To sound even more professional, use the formal telephone address: 'May I...?'

- 'May I help you?'
- 'May I take your name?'
- 'May I ask you to hold the line for a moment?'

Using 'May I' may take a little getting used to but just wait and see how impressed colleagues and clients are when you use it. If you don't feel comfortable with 'May I...?', you can ask 'How can I help you?' instead.

## Telephone do's and don'ts

- If the phone rings while you are attending to a client, remember who 'arrived' first. Ask if your present client minds if you answer the phone. The chances are that she won't, but it's good manners to ask.

- If a client comes into your salon while you are on the phone, always acknowledge her with a nod and smile.

- Answering the phone too quickly can surprise your caller. Leaving the phone ringing too long can aggravate your caller. Aim to answer the telephone between three and four rings.

- Never speak on the phone while eating or drinking or with *anything* in your mouth such as chewing gum or the end of a pencil. This is also a good rule when dealing with your clients in person!

- Modern phones can pick up sound from the handset. Never say anything over the phone that you do not want your caller to hear, even if you cover the mouthpiece or your phone has a 'hold' facility.

- Don't abandon your caller while she waits for someone to come to the phone. If she has to wait more than a few minutes, reassure her that the person is on her way. If there is a long delay, apologize and ask the caller if she would prefer to leave her name, number and a message – by this time, hopefully, the person will have arrived.

- Don't feel embarrassed to ask clients to repeat details or spell out names. To avoid confusion over the phone, use the phonetic or voice alphabet for spelling out letters.

**Table 8.1** The voice alphabet

| | | |
|---|---|---|
| a alpha | b bravo | c charlie |
| d delta | e echo | f foxtrot |
| g golf | h hotel | i india |
| j juliet | k kilo | l lima |
| m mike | n november | o oscar |
| p papa | q quebec | r romeo |
| s sierra | t tango | u uniform |
| v victor | w whiskey | x x-ray |
| y yankee | z zulu | |

## Screening calls

Screening a phone call means finding out if the caller really needs to speak personally to the person they ask for. Sometimes you will be able to deal with the caller yourself, without needing to interrupt a therapist or your manager.

When a caller asks to speak to a busy colleague by name, politely find out who the caller is by asking something like: 'May I ask who's calling?' If you don't recognize the name as a relation, friend, colleague or business associate, politely find out what the caller wants by asking: 'May I ask what it's about?'

Often the caller simply wants to make an appointment or ask for general information about salon treatments or products. Sometimes it will be a company representative wanting to sell products. Even if you cannot deal personally with the call, you then have information to give your colleague: 'It's Mrs Green phoning about advertising.'

## Telephone economy

If the extension you are phoning is busy, it is cheaper to hang up and try again later than to hold the line.

You should not make personal phone calls from your salon's phone. Your salon will receive itemized telephone bills which will show up unauthorized phone calls. If, for example, you need to make an emergency dental appointment from work, it is polite to ask your employer's permission first. This shows you are a responsible employee.

## Emergency services

You may be the nearest to the phone in a salon emergency. For example:

- A fire which is not quickly and easily put out with an extinguisher
- An intruder, such as a member of the public, who forces entry or becomes violent
- Someone involved in a serious accident
- Someone taken seriously ill.

Often people feel embarrassed about causing a fuss. If you are not sure how serious the accident or illness is, take charge of the situation and remember to put safety first. If in doubt, always call an ambulance, whether the client agrees or not.

---

**Emergency services**

When you dial 999, you will be asked:

1. Which service you require; fire, police or ambulance.
2. Your name and the address of the premises.
3. Brief details of the emergency.

---

## Answerphones and faxes

You must be able to use a fax machine and use and speak to an answerphone. Be careful not to lose answerphone messages. You may have to record an answerphone message. Speak slowly and clearly and include:

| Name of salon | 'Hello, Complexions |
| Reason for recorded message | is closed. |
| Instructions for caller | Please leave your name, number and message after the tone. |
| Your action | Your message will be dealt with promptly in the morning. |
| Thank the caller | Thank you for calling Complexions.' |

**Table 8.2**
An answerphone message

## Nuisance calls

Beauty salons and similar businesses occasionally get nuisance or obscene phone calls. These calls are generally not targeted at individuals. The male callers phone salons simply because they want to be sure a woman answers. Some callers want to shock, most want sexual gratification. All are hoping for a response.

Their motives are usually obvious from the start. More rarely, the caller will begin the conversation normally. If you get an obscene phone call at your salon:

- Stay calm.
- Don't make any further response to the caller.
- Gently lay the handset beside the phone.
- After a few minutes, gently replace the handset.
- If the phone rings again, lift the handset but don't speak. If it's a client, she will speak first.

Making a nuisance or obscene call is a criminal offence. Report all nuisance and obscene calls to the telephone company, for example British Telecom's malicious calls specialist bureau. The number is listed at the front of the phone book. In extreme cases, also report the offence to the police.

# Talking to your client

In the salon, conversation during treatment is for the benefit of the client and makes up part of the treatment. This doesn't mean you can't join in the chat, add your own comments and enjoy a joke.

Chatting with clients may seem an easy thing to do, but it's a salon skill to be learned like any other. If you lack this skill, no matter how competent you are, clients will find it difficult to get along with you. Conversation during treatment must always take second place to performing the treatment. Don't stop work to talk and don't let the conversation distract you from your work. If either of these things happen often, maybe your conversation is focused on you rather than your client.

## How to speak

Having 'empathy' means putting yourself in someone else's position and imagining how she feels. Think about each new client. Is she the type of person to feel intimidated or impressed by technical explanations of treatments? Notice the type of language and words she uses.

**Figure 8.1**
Ensure your
conversation is
focused on your
client, not you.

To make her feel at home, use similar ones when you speak to her. Many empathetic people do this naturally. It's a technique called 'mirroring'.

## What to talk about

You have a choice. You can have a general conversation about something that interests your client or you can discuss something specific to treatment. For example, when doing a manicure, you can ask your client about her hands and nails. This is often the best option for new clients or clients you can't find much in common with. Most people enjoy talking about themselves and will happily chat to you about their weight, skin or nails.

## How to start a conversation

> **Did you know?**   You can become a good conversationalist by imagining your client has the words '*Make me feel important*' written on her forehead. In conversation, say 'you' at least twice as often as you say 'I'.

As you get to know clients, conversation will happen naturally and you will soon look forward to catching up on your clients' news. But to begin with, let your client take the lead with conversation. If she doesn't speak, encourage her by making a general comment. Try one of the following most popular topics of salon conversation:

- 'What work do you do?' Most people are happy to comment on their work.
- 'Do you have children?' If the client's children are grown-up, ask about grandchildren.
- 'How are you keeping?' Many clients will have something to say about their health.

**Figure 8.2**
Let your client
take the lead in
conversation

If you are really stuck, there's always the weather. Commenting on the weather can lead on to conversations about holidays or weekend activities, but don't begin with them. Most people don't have diaries full of outings. You may annoy them by assuming they do.

## How to manage the conversation

Once the conversation has started, don't natter on madly. This will be tiring for you and your client.

- Keep the conversation low-key and relaxed.
- Short pauses are natural. There is no need to fill them with chatter.
- In the salon environment you must get along with all types of people. You'll find this easier if your keep your personal views and opinions in the background.
- Your aim is to relax your client. That's why it's generally best to avoid topics that provoke strong feeling such as politics, religion or sex.
- Be sure all your comments are appropriate. Avoid jokey comments that could be taken the wrong way.

> **Remember:** Some people are naturally skilled at entertaining, always able to recount an amusing story. If this is you, be careful not to offend your audience of one and never make fun of other clients.

## Note social details

Remembering each client's social details can be difficult until you get to know them all. Until then, it's fine to pencil a few discreet notes onto their **record cards**. For example, you may note where your client went on holiday, the names of her children or an important event such as moving house. To avoid asking repeatedly about old events, be sure to rub out the note when it no longer applies.

## When to listen

Being a responsive listener has several advantages over talking:

- People's life experiences are interesting. Often you'll learn something.
- Listening can help you improve your practical skills.
- Listening can help you sell products your client wants or needs.
- Listening is less tiring than talking.

If your client enjoys talking, listen and make the occasional sympathetic comment. Some people like to recount entertaining stories. Don't interrupt them or try to compete with a funnier story of your own.

Never pretend to listen while thinking of something else. Your client will quickly notice this and feel rightly offended. Paying less than full attention when someone is speaking to you is unprofessional, not to mention rude.

## When to be silent

Don't talk too much to your client during massage since the aim is physical and mental relaxation. If your client is chatty during massage, encourage her to gain the most benefit from treatment by saying something like: 'This is your time to relax now.'

Some clients like to be left to relax during a face mask, others prefer you to stay and keep them company. (Claustrophobic clients must never be left alone under a face mask or in a small beauty cubicle.) Some clients like to relax with their thoughts; others like to be entertained or to entertain.

## Speak with enthusiasm

Enthusiasm is infectious. Speak positively about treatments and what they can achieve. If you don't sound as though you believe treatment will do wonders for your client, don't expect her to be too enthusiastic.

# Ask your client for information

Learn from your tutors, colleagues ... and your clients. Clients are experts on themselves. Talk to your client; she may tell you which colours suit her, why she puts on weight or breaks her nails. Add this information to your professional knowledge to help you decide on the best product or treatment for her.

Client information can be vital. For example, a cosmetic your client is using may be responsible for skin or nail damage. Facial creams containing retinol (to reduce the appearance of wrinkles), benzoyl peroxide (to combat acne) and calcium thioglycollate (depilatory cream) can act as **irritants**. Unsuitable astringents can badly effect skin texture.

Your client's information can:

- Ensure she will be pleased with treatment results. For example, during make-up, it's useful to check that she likes the shade of foundation you have applied.
- Prevent complaint. For instance, is she happy with the position you have marked for her ear-piercing? You may have to alter the marks several times before she is

completely happy but if she has a say in the position, she'll never return to complain.

■ Help you identify one or more specific areas for improvement so that you can ensure your client sees improvement after treatment.

■ Help you improve your practical skills. Does she feel a 'pull' on hairs during **electro-epilation**? This indicates they have been insufficiently treated.

## 'Salon speak'

Have you noticed how some clients wince and grimace as the skin is painlessly stretched before epilation or tweezing? It's a fact that tense, nervous people feel pain more because they are concentrating on it.

Waxing, ear-piercing and **electro-epilation** can be uncomfortable. Notice the word 'uncomfortable' and the phrase 'can be' in the last sentence. The sentence would have sounded very different if it had read:

*Waxing, ear-piercing and **electro-epilation** are painful.*

If you were a first-time **electro-epilation** client, which sentence would you prefer to hear?

During treatment, the words you use will make a big difference to how your client 'feels' the treatment. Of course, you can't pretend a treatment such as ear-piercing is completely painless because your client will never trust your word again. On the other hand, she doesn't want to hear you say with brutal honesty, that 'it stings like fury'.

The aim of 'salon speak' is to relax and reassure your client so that she feels the least discomfort. So, choose your words carefully.

■ 'Needle' is an old-fashioned term for today's disposable **electro-epilation** probes which are as fine as fuse wire. Some people have a fear of needles. Replace this word with 'probe' which sounds far less painful.

■ Say '**micropigmentation**' or 'semi-permanent make-up' not 'tattoo'.

■ Answer 'Will this hurt?' by saying something like: 'You may feel a slight tingle' or 'it may feel a little warm'.

■ Say 'discomfort' never 'pain'.

In time, these words will come so naturally to you that you will find yourself asking a new mother, 'Was the birth uncomfortable?'

## Honesty with tact

There are honest therapists and there are honest, successful therapists. The second sort temper their honesty with tact. Clients respect honesty but they also come to your salon to feel good about themselves. With a little forethought, both can be successfully combined. When describing skin types, for example, chose words that sound flattering.

■ Say 'fine lines', 'facial lines' or 'expression lines' not 'wrinkles' or 'crow's feet'.

■ 'Fine skin' sounds more attractive 'thin skin'.

■ Say 'olive' rather than 'sallow'.

■ Say 'mature skin' not 'crêpey' or 'wrinkled'.

■ Say 'congested' not 'spotty'.

■ Say 'blocked pores' or '**comedones**' not 'blackheads'.

■ On price lists and promotions, refer to 'Senior Citizens' not 'OAPs'.

Be tactful when using or recommending remedial or corrective cosmetics such as concealers. If you feel your client would benefit from the application of concealer (and who wouldn't?), don't draw attention to this baldly, even if she does so herself. She is, no doubt, already aware of her facial flaws and blemishes. Don't make her feel even more self-conscious. You could say: 'This concealer is excellent if you ever get dark circles after a late night. I'll show you how to apply it.'

If your client complains directly to you about a facial or figure flaw, act as if you didn't really notice it until she pointed it out. Your client will instantly feel 50 per cent more confident about her appearance – an excellent result and treatment hasn't even begun yet!

Most clients are interested to find out about remedial and corrective cosmetics. However, some clients whom you think may benefit from remedial camouflage are comfortable with their natural appearances. This is a healthy attitude so be extra tactful about suggesting any form of remedial camouflage such as theatrical putty for deep or raised scarring or cover creams for birthmarks. First, establish whether your client feels she needs them by asking an open question during treatment such as: 'How do you feel about your birthmark?'

## Getting technical

Beauty therapy has its share of technical and chemical terms. It's true that you can perform a satisfactory treatment without knowing the name of the active ingredient or the technical term for the process. But you'll be more professional if you do. So, don't just skip over unfamiliar words in your textbooks.

It's easier to learn a long chemical name or technical term if you break it into syllables and find out how to pronounce each syllable. For example, the active ingredient in self-tanning cream is dihydroxyacetone which breaks down into: di-hydroxy-acetone. You'll soon find these names will sound as familiar as your own! You will then be in an excellent position to answer your client's questions fully – for they will ask.

---

**Remember:** If you don't know the answer to your client's question, never bluff. This will damage your professional reputation. Tell your client that she's asked a good question. Find out the answer and let her know next time she visits.

---

### What do you think?

1. Try this with a colleague or friend. Ask your friend to close her eyes while you repeat the same phrases first with a smile, then with a scowl. Keep everything the same except the change in expression. What does this tell you about your expression in relationship to the sound of your voice?

2. If you use medical or scientific terminology make sure you use it correctly. What is wrong with the following sentence? This lotion contains tea tree oil which has an anti-bactericidal effect.

3. What do you think makes a good conversationalist? Take turns practising being 'good conversationalists' with your colleagues, family and friends. Choose a subject for conversation then gain one point every time your opponent uses the word 'I'.

# Chapter Nine

# Working with Colleagues and Related Professionals

*Don't restrict professionalism to clients alone.*

## Working with colleagues

As a professional working with the public, you must develop the skill of getting along with all sorts of people. Why not practise with your colleagues? Getting along well with your colleagues will help to make a friendly and relaxed salon atmosphere which clients will enjoy.

**Figure 9.1**
Develop a good working relationship with colleagues

## Be a good team worker

Be prepared to pitch in. If you help your colleagues whenever you can, they will value you as a good team worker. This could mean sharing out a sick colleague's appointments or rearranging your appointments at short notice to fit in a double-booking.

In busy salons, time off and holidays need careful arranging so that business is not disrupted. Always check with your salon manager before booking a holiday. Ask for time off with as much notice as possible.

**Figure 9.2**
Give as much notice as possible for holiday dates

## Respect different working techniques

Different working procedures and practices are fine as long as they give professional results and professional standards of hygiene are kept up. Some salons prefer all staff to use the same working procedures.

## Suggesting salon improvements

As you work, you may think up improvements to your salon's working practices. You may spot breaches in safety and hygiene. Don't sit around and hope for improvement – it may never come. It is *always* professional to mention points for improvement to your salon tutor or manager *but be tactful*, particularly if you are new to the salon. Chose the most suitable moment and be careful never to cause embarrassment.

Begin by asking a general question about the practice that you are concerned about. Follow this up by offering your suggestion as an improvement to the system rather than a criticism. For example, ask how the spa pool is maintained. Follow this up by asking when it would be practical for you to drain it down and scrub it. Compliment the salon colour scheme, then ask when the woodwork is due for repainting.

Suggest an improvement to hygiene so that the salon can look 'even more impressive', or working practices can be 'even safer'. Generally, your manager will be pleased for you to take the initiative and implement salon improvements.

Never show disagreement with or disapproval of a colleague, or criticize her in front of another colleague or client. Sort out a query or refinement of working practice personally, in private. If you think a practice may cause immediate injury to someone, call your colleague urgently to reception where you can speak to her privately.

## Respect colleagues' clientele

It's fine for clients to switch therapists if they want to, but guard against 'poaching' your colleagues' clients. If your salon pays commission on treatments, this will lower their wages.

If your salon pays commission on sales, be fair when deciding who earned the sale. Usually it is the person who spent most time with the client rather than the one who took the payment. This also applies to sales of treatment courses and gift vouchers.

If you work on commission, it's unprofessional to turn a client away because you cannot personally fit her appointment in. Neither should you make her wait too long for you to become available. Offer to book her in with a colleague.

## Don't get offended

Salons are very busy places. When you need help from a colleague, it will come much more quickly if you ask politely. Try it. If your salon manager or tutor asks or tells you to do something quickly or brusquely, don't feel offended. It's not because she doesn't value you. It's more likely that she's busy and anxious to fulfil her responsibilities to her clients and staff. These busy times are when she will most value your help and support.

> **Remember:** Don't develop double standards. If you can't stand 'being told what to do', don't expect your staff to do as you ask when it's your turn to be in charge.

While you are training, colleagues may ask you to do different jobs at the same time. If this happens, explain the situation and offer to do the most urgent task first. If you have too much to do, ask for help.

## Sort out disputes

From time to time, colleagues have disagreements or difficulties in working together. This is when professionalism with colleagues is most important. Try to solve problems and misunderstandings by talking them through at an appropriate time and place. Remember to use your listening skills and try to come to an understanding or compromise.

## Employing staff

Never rely on 'gut feeling' alone when taking on employees. Follow your instincts but don't rely on them to spot dishonesty or even psychosis. Always double-check all information.

- Ask to see *original* certificates of qualification. If your therapist has failed any component of her exam, your insurance will not be valid.
- Ask for two work or character references and be sure to check them both, *especially* if the applicant claims to have worked abroad.
- Begin employment with a six-week probationary period, just in case things don't work out.
- For a £10 fee, the police will confirm your applicant does not have a criminal record.

## Quiz – Are you professional with colleagues?

1.  *As a trainee, you begin a manicure on Mrs D while a qualified therapist begins a pedicure. You notice that Mrs D has the fungal infection **tinea** unguium (ringworm of the nail) on her toenails. You know this condition is contagious and contra-indicated to pedicure. Do you:*

    a)  Politely excuse yourself from your client to fetch a piece of equipment, then call the therapist to the reception desk where you discreetly explain what you noticed?

    b)  Say nothing and hope the infection doesn't spread to other clients?

    c)  Mouth and point the information to your colleague, hoping your client won't notice?

2.  *As a salon manager, you overhear a trainee giving inaccurate information to a client who has asked about sunbed treatment. Do you:*

    a)  Tactfully adjust the trainee's advice so that the client leaves correctly informed and the trainee is saved embarrassment, then ensure the trainee gets suitable backup training to stop it happening again?

    b)  Say nothing; it won't hurt for just one client to be told wrong information?

    c)  Sternly reprimand the trainee in front of the client to show off your knowledge and impress the client?

3.  *As a trainee you are watching a qualified colleague do a make-over on a friend of hers, out of hours. She wants to moisten a cotton bud to remove a blob of mascara but finds she has no water to hand. She sucks the cotton bud to moisten it. Do you:*

    a)  Say nothing but make a mental note never to be unprofessional even with friends?

    b)  Smile weakly and say that's just what you would have done under the circumstance?

    c)  Gasp in horror, point and tell the friend that that is so unhygienic!?

4.  *You see a colleague just about to help a client onto the sunbed. From a previous consultation, you know the client has recently had laser treatment for cervical cancer. Do you:*

    a)  Discreetly hand your colleague the sunbed contra-indication list, point to the relevant line and suggest her client recheck it.

    b)  Say nothing; it's really none of your business.

    c)  Shout across the salon to your colleague, 'Get her off, get her off! She's had treatment for cervical cancer!'

## Answers

**If you chose 'a's** – Your colleagues will be delighted with your professionalism.
**If you chose 'b's** – Always act professionally and never neglect health and safety to avoid embarrassment.
**If you chose 'c's** – I hope I never work with you!

# Liaising with related professionals

Once you are qualified, clients will sometimes ask you for advice and support on matters other than beauty. Remember only to advise on what you are qualified in. If need be, suggest your client see a more suitable professional such as a doctor or counsellor.

To **liaise** (pronounced lee-ayze) means 'to co-operate' or 'act as a link'. During your career, you will need to **liaise** with other professions, most commonly, doctors (see Chapter Eleven – Medical Conditions in the Salon).

Find out what other related professionals do and how they can help various conditions. If you get the chance, ask professionals about their work. Keep a book at reception with details of reputable local health professionals. Other professionals you may liaise with include:

- chiropodists ('chiro' is pronounced with a hard 'c'), foot skin specialists
- dentists
- physiotherapists, specializing in manipulation, massage, heat treatment and remedial exercise
- chiropractors, specializing in joint and spinal adjustment
- osteopaths, specializing in bone alignment
- alternative health practitioners, e.g. acupuncturists and homeopaths
- counsellors and therapists
- plastic surgeons. Advise against self-referral (when clients answer an advert). Recommend your client consult only a surgeon qualified in plastic surgery. Her GP can refer her to a member of the British Association of Aesthetic Plastic Surgeons – BAAPS.

# Relations with competitors

Few salons have a town or village clientele all to themselves, these days. No doubt, there will be another beauty salon near yours. Competition keeps standards high. Be professional when you speak about or deal with other salons. It's always unprofessional to criticize another salon or beauty therapist.

- Visit a newly opened salon and introduce yourself.
- If you have opened a new salon, visit existing salons and introduce yourself.
- Never disparage (make bad remarks about) another salon or therapist to a client.
- If your client disparages another salon, you can listen but don't join in – silence can speak for itself.

If you can't help a client, for example you don't offer a particular treatment or are fully booked on the prospective client's wedding day, suggest she try a nearby salon. This will show that the client is *always* your first priority. You should keep your clients because you are the best, not because your clients don't know of another salon!

Being on friendly terms with neighbouring salons can be very useful. My ear-piercing gun once jammed, mid-pierce – guess where I dashed off to …?

## *Dealing with sales companies and reps*

Company sales representatives are known as **reps**. They may or may not have a sound training in beauty therapy. Remember their sole aim in life is to sell. Be ruthless with **reps**.

- Only see a **rep** if you are interested in the product.
- Ensure **reps** always make an appointment, even if they call when you're not busy.
- Allocate them a certain amount of time and make them stick to it.
- Don't be afraid to interrupt sales patter to ask what you need to know.
- Don't let your **rep** dictate what your salon stocks or sells.
- Never be talked into buying stock or equipment you don't need or won't be able to sell.
- Don't be afraid to negotiate yourself a better deal.
- Learn from **reps**; they are generally very accomplished sellers.

Think of it as a one-way relationship. Tap into their expertise and skill if you need it, then send them on their way. There is always another cosmetic company but your **rep** needs *your* business to survive.

### What do you think?

1. Your rep recommends a skin-bleaching product with the active ingredient hydroquinone. You know that hydroquinone can cause more pigmentation problems (vitiligo) than it solves even at the 2 per cent concentration allowed by **EU** regulations. It may also be **carcinogenic**. What would you say to the rep?

2. What do you think of this stockist's explanation of cellulite? Is it designed to inform?
   '...When a metabolic problem arises, an imbalance is caused in the absorption and elimination of residues. This makes the mucopolysaccharide molecules polymerize and develop into clusters of more complex molecules that increase the viscosity of the fundamental substance. This is how cellulite first develops.'

# PART TWO

# *Professionalism with Clients*

# Chapter Ten

# *Look After your Client*

*Caring for your client makes the difference between a competent worker and a true professional.*

## Keep your client looking good

A visit to the beauty therapist is generally a luxury. Make beauty treatments as pleasurable as possible, even when there is some discomfort involved. This may seem obvious, but poorly performed treatments can leave your client looking or feeling worse than when she arrived!

### Protect clothes and underclothes

Many salon preparations such as wax, oil, sugar paste, cream, nail polish and tint can damage or stain your client's clothes. Even talc can mark. Treat all your client's clothes as if they are brand new and expensive.

- Try to avoid creasing her clothes too much. Provide clothes hangers and use them.
- Accidents do happen. Make sure the clothes your client keeps on during treatment are well protected with clean towels – a towel is far cheaper to replace than your client's designer outfit.

---

**Did you know?** Hair lacquer can act as a solvent and can sometimes prevent tint from permanently staining clothing. If you drop eyelash tint on your client's clothes, ask her to remove the garment immediately. Quickly scrape off the excess tint and immediately spray liberally with hair lacquer. Then have the garment dry cleaned.

---

- Use tissues to protect clothes. Tucking a tissue over a turned-up sleeve during a manicure massage will stop it becoming soiled with hand cream.
- Use tissues to protect underwear. Tucking a tissue over each bra-strap during a facial or massage treatment will stop them becoming soiled with oil or cream. Likewise, protect pants during bikini-line waxing.

- When applying moistened faradic pads, don't moisten the pads so much that drips run into your client's underwear – how would you like to sit for 45 minutes in damp knickers?
- After body massage – unless the client prefers otherwise – remove excess oil with cotton wool pads moistened with toner to prevent it soiling clothes. This is also a useful way of waking a client who has fallen asleep during treatment.

## Cover hair

Covering your client's hair may sometimes flatten a blow-dried style or hair set. However, this is better than getting oil, cream or eyelash tint in it. The exception is when applying make-up; your client may already have her hair styled so use a thin plastic hairband or clips to hold her fringe back while you apply foundation and powder. Take the hairband off as soon as possible to avoid spoiling her hairstyle.

- During facial treatments or back massage, protect your client's hair with a loose turban, adjustable cap or hair net. Wrap a strip of crêpe bandage or an adjustable headband securely over the edge to prevent oil seeping into her hairline.
- Be flexible. If your client is particularly concerned about her hairstyle, use only the headband but take extra care not to drip preparations onto her hair.
- Use a tissue to protect your client's hair from drips when applying lash or brow tint.
- Clients sometimes ask to borrow a brush or comb after treatment. Lend a plastic comb that can be sterilized along with the other salon equipment.

## Eyes

Always ask if your facial client wears contact lenses – with a little practice, you will be able to spot them. Always invite her to remove her lenses before treatment. Your client will feel discomfort if cosmetics become trapped between her eye and the lens. Some clients prefer *not* to remove their lenses during facial treatment. However, insist she remove them during **UV** treatment and eyelash tinting. During **UV** treatment, the plastic lenses could melt onto her eye. During tinting, if tint becomes trapped below the lens, it could burn her eye.

> **Remember:**   Contact lenses left in glasses of water in the sun bed area are likely to be drunk! Keep a sterilized lens container (from the chemist) for clients who forget theirs.

- Any substance that gets into your client's eyes will sting. If there is any chance of splashing products into your clients' eyes – for example, during electrical brushing treatment – always protect her eyes with damp cotton wool pads as you work.
- Treat the entire eye area gently, particularly when applying or blending eye shadow over the lid covering the eyeball, which is very sensitive to pressure.
- Disturb the thin, delicate skin around the eye area as little as possible during treatment. This area is very prone to wrinkling and your older clients will be very

aware of this. Apply cream to this area with your ring finger (your third finger) only. This is your weakest finger and produces least pressure. Advise your clients to do the same.

■ Some oily eye make-up removers leave eyes bleary. Try to find one that doesn't.

■ During eyelash tint, only mix sufficient oxidant – hydrogen peroxide – for **oxidation** to occur. Too much will result in a runny mixture and hydrogen peroxide will cause severe stinging if it runs into your client's eyes. For this reason, don't leave your client while the tint develops.

■ Activated lash tint quickly stains skin. The stain is not permanent, but will look unsightly for about a week. Always protect the skin around your client's eyes and brows with a thin smear of petroleum jelly. Once the treatment is complete, be sure to remove every trace of tint. Your client could easily rub tint residue into her eyes once she has left the salon. This will sting as well as stain.

■ Don't over-chlorinate spa pools. Measure the amount of chemical carefully. Pools with too much chlorine result in streaming eyes and can damage tinted or permed hair.

## Maintaining appearance between treatments

During a course of facial **electro-epilation**, your client will no longer be able to pluck her facial hair. She is certain to feel very self-conscious for a few months before the hair growth begins to thin. Be sure to suggest an alternative way to maintain her appearance and explain that as hairs become finer, less maintenance will be needed.

■ She can trim the regrowth closely with nail scissors.

■ She can shave the area, so long as she leaves a couple of days' growth before her next appointment. Close shaving and cover-cream is a very useful option if your client has somewhere special to go.

■ She can bleach so long as this doesn't make the hairs too difficult for you to see.

# Salon preparations which can cause discomfort

You can't beat first-hand experience for learning how things feel. Unfortunately, it's not always possible for colleagues to demonstrate every preparation, technique and treatment on you. If possible, use the preparations and equipment on yourself to check that they don't feel unpleasant or cause discomfort.

■ Some face masks can feel claustrophobic. Check your client isn't claustrophobic before applying a thick or heavy face mask.

■ Never leave your client's skin feeling greasy with moisturiser or massage oil. Always blot excess preparations with a tissue.

■ Surgical spirit dehydrates facial skin and smells clinical. Use antiseptic lotion to prevent infection and facial astringent (toner containing alcohol) to degrease before facial waxing or tweezing.

■ Potassium hydroxide used in cuticle remover is caustic and can burn. Rinse this off your client's skin thoroughly after use.

■ Some abrasive skin exfoliants can cause soreness on sensitive, thin or dry skin. Use a peeling cream only on these skin types.

*Irritants and sensitizers*

Any product can cause discomfort if it acts as an **irritant** or sensitizes your client to an ingredient in the product. Many clients claim to have 'sensitive skin'. Find out what they mean by 'sensitive'. Are they sensitive to a particular ingredient or product, or do they have a 'delicate' or 'easily irritated' skin? Even if products state they don't contain perfume or colour they can still contain well-known skin **irritants** such as the preservative paraben.

- Some aromatherapy oils can act as **irritants** and **sensitizers**.
- Skin care ranges which are labelled 'hypoallergenic' hold no guarantees. 'Hypo' means 'low' and 'allergenic' means 'allergy-causing' so hypoallergenic only means 'less likely to cause allergy'.
- Use 'aqueous cream' (from the chemist) on clients who say they have very sensitive skin or whose skin is sore due to diagnosed skin conditions such as **seborrhoea** or acne. Aqueous cream is a very simple water-based cream. It isn't very exciting to anyone with 'normal' skin but to a client with painful, irritated skin, it is soothing and lubricating. It can be used as a cleanser, face mask and moisturiser. Use only distilled water as toner.

If your client's skin reacts to an **irritant** in one of your preparations, her skin will generally show signs of **erythema** and **oedema** due to the release of **histamine**. Reassure her as you remove all traces of the product using aqueous cream. Apply a cooling compress – such as moist cotton wool – until her skin feels cool again. Mark on your client's treatment card, clearly in bold red pen, that your client reacted to the product.

---

**Remember:** Anaphylactic shock is an extremely severe allergic reaction and very rare. It usually occurs when the allergen is eaten or injected (such as a bee sting). If your client turns very pale or has any difficulty in breathing, call an ambulance immediately.

---

## Poor technique which can cause discomfort

The following examples of poor technique may not damage your client but they will all cause her discomfort.

*Body treatment*

- Make sure your client isn't cold. A chilly treatment can never be an enjoyable treatment.
- Make sure your hands are warm before you begin massage.
- Massage movements are designed to counter (go the opposite way to) gravity because this relaxes the muscle and feels wonderful! Movements that drag the muscle and skin in the same direction as gravity feel dreadful. Your client won't pay good money for a bad massage.
- During massage, take care your percussion movements aren't heavy-handed. Bashing down onto bone is painful and likely to cause bruising which you may never see – unless your client returns to complain. Hack and clap with a light flicking movement – imagine the skin is red-hot to the touch.

**Figure 10.1**
A couch
incorporating a
breathing hole

- Ideally, your massage couch will have a breathing hole. This design is more comfortable for your massage client. Also, the **trapezius** muscle in the shoulders and neck is more efficiently massaged with the head laid straight.

- Body wraps must be applied tightly, but not too tightly. Your client must feel comfortable and able to breathe easily. Be careful not to restrict her circulation flow, particularly at elbow and knee joints.

- If you need to leave your client, such as during electronic muscle exercise, clip a timer to your uniform so you don't lose track of the time or get held up at reception.

## Facial treatment

- Treat facial skin with great respect and advise your client to do the same.

- The **trachea** is very sensitive to pressure. Remember to cup your hands over your client's **trachea** as you massage or apply cream to her neck.

- Don't press hard over bone or soft tissue when expressing **comedones** through the hole of a **comedone** extractor. Use a gentle rocking motion.

- Remember that the area over the sinuses, the tip of the nose and the borders of the lips are very sensitive to pressure. Gently circle the rim of the **comedone** extractor over sensitive areas containing blocked pores. This helps prevent comedones forming.

- During facial massage, notice how some facial muscles, such as the **corrugator supercilii** and **masseter**, benefit from deep pressure and some, such as the **platysma**, can only take light pressure.
- Make your client's steam treatment a comfortable experience. Steam flowing from chin to forehead is an effective position for steaming the T-zone but some clients find steam flowing from forehead to chin more comfortable.
- When tinting and shaping eyebrows, always tint first. Tint will sting freshly plucked brows.

## Waxing

- Bruising during waxing is a common mistake. Perfect your waxing technique so that you never cause a bruise.
- By all means, be economical with **consumables** like wax strips but never at the expense of your client's comfort. This is false economy. Use a fresh wax strip on the under-arm or bikini-line area, even if it's only for a few hairs.
- Spread wax as thinly as possible. This reduces the 'pull' on the skin.
- Always stretch the skin below the strip and remove it backward onto itself, as close to the skin surface as you can. Never pull upwards, this is very painful as well as ineffective at removing hair.
- Never wax over hair-free areas! For example, don't wax over the vein in the crook of the arm or back of the knee where you will surely bruise your client.
- Thin skin with a good blood supply such as the under-arm or groin area is far more likely to bruise if waxed over twice. Never wax over the same area three times. If hairs remain, remove quickly with **automatic tweezers** – your client will barely feel this since the hairs will have been loosened by waxing.
- Since you don't have three hands to wax triangular areas with, it's fine to ask your client to help pull the skin taut during bikini-line waxing. In fact, this gives nervous clients something to put their energy into!
- Remember, it is impossible to wax round corners and therefore impossible to wax over the angle of the groin with one stroke! If you accidentally apply wax to both angles at the same time wax, one surface at a time and get sticky fingers.

## Manicure and pedicure

- Cuticles are delicate and are easily torn and inflamed. *Gently* free your client's cuticle from the nail plate.
- Don't poke under the cuticle into the nail matrix. The nail matrix is *very* sensitive to pressure and also prone to infection. Heavy-handed cuticle work can result in ridged nails, white marks and **paronychia**.
- Cuticle knives aren't sharp but can cause damage to delicate tissue. Always work with your cuticle knife blade moistened and flat to the nail.
- Manicure treatment often loosens bits of cuticle from the nail plate. Carefully trim these to prevent your client developing painful **agnails**.
- Some cuticles need trimming but don't clip them all off routinely, this can encourage **agnails**. Avoid tearing cuticles; always make a clean cut using *sharp* cuticle clippers.

- Buff and file nails in one direction only. Buffing and filing backwards and forwards creates uncomfortable heat in the nail due to friction.
- Ensure that the temperature of the manicure or pedicure water is comfortable. Of course, it must not be too hot but water is equally uncomfortable if it is too cool or quickly gets cold.

### Electro-epilation

- Keep nails short. If you make half-moon patterns on your client's skin, your nails are too long.
- Stretch the skin enough to insert the probe accurately but there's no need to pull or press down onto the skin vigorously, causing discomfort.
- Choose a suitably sized **electro-epilation** probe for the diameter of the hair to be epilated. Using too thick a probe can cause bruising. If you bend 0.003 size probes, you need to improve your insertion technique.
- Your **electro-epilation** client will have to accept some degree of discomfort for treatment to be effective. However, if treatment is performed correctly, the sensation will be from the heat emitted from the end of the probe, not from the probe insertion.
- Accurate insertion is vital for a comfortable epilation treatment. Although you are working 'blind', with practice you will be able to 'feel' inside the follicle. Too shallow an insertion may mean you inserted into the sebaceous gland. Inserting too deeply will pierce the base of the follicle. There is really no excuse for missing the mouth of the follicle – that's the part you can see! If you have trouble with insertion, visit the optician.
- **Electro-epilation** can cause permanent freckling if performed over areas of **chloasma**. Do a **patch test** before treatment and don't treat if affected.

## Body language and feedback

Since preparations, equipment and treatment technique can cause discomfort for your client, remember to ask her for **feedback** and watch her **body language**. You will need both sets of information to judge accurately how your client is enjoying her treatment.

### Ask for feedback

Just because your client doesn't complain it doesn't necessarily mean you are doing a good job. A few clients will volunteer information about their treatment. Most need to be invited to comment. Some clients will suffer discomfort and even pain without complaint.

Asking for **feedback** from your client during treatment means asking her if she is comfortable or if something is too hot or too cold. This is a valuable way of ensuring your client isn't in discomfort, or worse, in line for injury. It's also a good way of monitoring how good your treatment is.

No matter how experienced you become, never rely on **body language** alone when performing a high-risk treatment such as applying depilatory wax or paraffin wax. Always ask your client if treatment is comfortable.

## Check body language

Watching your client's **body language** during treatment can tell you what *she* doesn't. The following are all signs of discomfort:

- shivering
- frowning
- shuffling uncomfortably
- swallowing hard
- screwed up eyes
- wincing
- clenched teeth
- pursed lips.

On the other hand, if she dozes, she's relaxed. If she snores – always deny this – she's really relaxed. Well done!

# Keep your client informed

Surprises aren't always pleasant! Your client will feel much more relaxed if she knows *before* you do it what you are going to do, why you are doing it, how long it's going to last and how it will feel.

## Explain electrical treatments fully

It's important to explain treatments clearly to clients, particularly treatment using electrical equipment. Many people are understandably nervous about being wired up to electrical appliances. Your client cannot have a relaxing treatment unless she understands the treatment and feels reassured that it won't harm her.

**Figure 10.2**
Explain fully how electrical equipment works

> **Remember:** Encourage your client to ask questions. Some clients may have odd worries. For example, she may ask whether **electro-epilation** can cause cancer. Treat all questions seriously, and take care never to make your client feel foolish for asking.

## Tell your client what to expect

Be sure to explain beforehand the sensations your client will feel during treatment. For example, explain to your galvanic facial client that if she has several metal fillings, she will get a metallic taste in her mouth and this is nothing to worry about.

- If your client is nervous about electrical therapy, a short demonstration is worth a thousand words of reassurance. For example, early on in an **electro-epilation consultation**, it's often helpful to epilate a hair on your client's arm. Generally she will find this is quite bearable and will be much less nervous for her first appointment.

> **Remember:** A colourful diagram of the structure of the hair in the skin is very helpful for explaining to clients how **electro-epilation** works. It's important to explain to your client about regrowth, when to expect it, how much to expect and what to do with it.

- Applying unexpectedly cold or hot preparations during a facial can surprise your client. Tell your client in advance if a preparation is warmer or cooler than room temperature. This is particularly important if your client has eye pads on and cannot see.
- If you leave your client during treatment, so that she can relax, tell her how long you are leaving her for.

## Warn of temporary reaction or marking

Never perform a treatment that could damage your client. However, if correct treatment leaves a temporary mark, be sure your client knows this beforehand. Explain that the reaction is entirely normal and nothing to worry about.

- Waxing leaves red, raised bumps – **erythema** and **oedema** – for up to 12 hours after treatment.
- **Electro-epilation** leaves red, sometimes raised, bumps for a few hours after treatment.
- The blood supply to the eye area is dense. Even with best practice, there is a slight risk of causing a black-eye effect when electro-epilating eyebrows.
- **Red vein cauterization** can leave temporary 'bramble scratches' for up two weeks.
- A **milium** extraction may leave a pinprick scab for up to a week.
- **Micropigmentation** can cause temporary redness and swelling for up to 24 hours after treatment.

# Minimizing discomfort and normal reactions

**Electro-epilation**, waxing, tweezing and ear-piercing are bound to hurt your client a bit, however skilled you are. Try to keep discomfort to a minimum. Here are some ideas:

- Apply a warm cotton wool compress to brows before tweezing.

- **Automatic tweezers** can lessen tweezing discomfort because they speed up treatment and give a consistent, quick, clean pull.

- Pain receptors in the skin can be masked by activating pressure receptors. Apply pressure to the plucked area to disperse the stinging sensation.

- During electro-epilation, heat is used to destroy the hair follicle's hair-growing cells. A pad dampened with witch hazel can really help to cool the area you last treated while you work on the next. This also works well for tweezing.

> **Remember:** Areas where the skin is thin such as the lip-line, the throat, around the nipple and the groin are much more sensitive to the heat used in electro-epilation than, for example the chin or leg. If discomfort after treatment lasts longer than about 20 minutes, you may have used too high a current or overtreated the area.

- Sometimes clients with heavy brows suffer sneezing fits from prolonged tweezing. Eyebrow waxing can be a useful alternative; it's quicker for therapist and client.

- Always wax the knee bent so that the skin is taut.

- If your client complains about the red bumps from waxing, she can ask her pharmacist's advice about applying an over-the-counter 0.5 per cent hydrocortisone cream. Hydrocortisone is a steroid that reduces inflammation. The cream should be applied very sparingly.

- Notice which way the hairs grow *before* applying the wax, particularly in the bikini-line and under-arm area. This cuts out the need to wax over an area twice.

- Shorter hairs 'pull' less, which makes treatment far more comfortable – and less likely to bruise. Before waxing, trim **virgin** bikini and under-arm hair to 1cm long. Use round-bladed scissors so that you don't risk cutting skin. It is particularly helpful to trim hair growing towards the back of the bikini-line area, since this area is the most difficult to wax.

- Catch and free bikini-line hairs trapped under the pant-line with tweezers. This prevents the client pressing on the ends while you try to wax out the roots – ouch!

- Plan combined waxing treatments with comfort in mind. A client who books a full leg wax and bikini-line may prefer to have half her bikini-line waxed then one leg, followed by the remaining bikini-line and leg. Alternatively, she may prefer the bikini-line wax first. Either way, don't forget to wax everywhere!

- Help disguise **erythema** after hair removal by applying a tinted after-care lotion. This is particularly useful for **electro-epilation** clients but it can also be applied to waxed or plucked areas such as eyebrows.

- If your client complains of discomfort during waxing or **electro-epilation**, suggest she avoid booking her appointments at the same time as or just before her menstrual period, when she may be more sensitive to pain.
- Clients who are nervous of discomfort or feel a lot of discomfort can take a painkiller such as paracetamol before they arrive for treatment. An anti-inflammatory painkiller such as aspirin will also help to reduce erythema and oedema but can slow blood clotting which may slightly lessen the effectiveness of electro-epilation. (Some people are allergic to aspirin.)

> **Remember:** You are not qualified to give out any form of medication. Never give clients or staff any form of medication; even over-the-counter painkillers.

## Minimize embarrassment

Beauty treatments which are very familiar to you may be a new and possibly daunting experience for your client. Make sure it is not an embarrassing one by doing your best to ensure she doesn't feel uncomfortable or vulnerable.

### What you say

Are you sensitive about aspects of your appearance? Think how discussing the following subjects may make your client feel embarrassed, self-conscious or uncomfortable:

- age – it's more discreet to ask your client's date of birth than her age
- mature skin-type and facial lines
- excess weight
- loss of skin tone or muscle tone
- cellulite
- superfluous hair
- problem skin conditions such as acne.

Use tact and discretion when introducing or discussing subjects your client may feel sensitive about.

### Dos and don'ts for keeping your client feeling relaxed

- During a manicure, don't rest your client's hand on your knee! Place her hand on a cushion covered with a towel.
- Do tell your client clearly what you want her to take off for treatment. If you are vague, she will worry that she has taken off too much or not enough.
- Do be discreet when treating intimate areas. For example, don't ask your client to bend both knees at once during bikini-line waxing; cover each breast immediately after you finish treating it.
- Many clients feel vulnerable without underwear, particularly pants. If your client needs to take off her pants for treatment, do provide a disposable paper pair for her to change into. Alternatively, suggest she bring an old pair with her.

- Never show surprise or horror at anything a client confides to you.
- Never show distaste or disgust at a client's physique or physical **anomaly**.
- Don't stand and watch your client undress. Ideally, leave the room for a few moments.
- Don't stand directly in front of your client when taking body measurements, particularly when taking the bust and buttock measurement. Stand to one side.
- Don't repeat body measurements aloud as you note them on the record card – unless there is a reduction. This may make an overweight client feel self-conscious. If she wants to know her measurements or weight, show her on the card.

## Considerate covering

If you spend all day staring at bras and knickers, you're not covering your clients considerately. Whatever your attitude to the naked body, remember that it's natural and normal for clients, particularly older ones, to feel vulnerable or embarrassed when naked or in underwear. Avoid causing embarrassment by making use of towels and blankets. It is especially vital for male therapists to pay very strict attention to discreet client covering.

> **Remember:** Don't leave your client exposed to cold *or* embarrassment. You can't offend her by too much covering.

- Provide a dressing robe as well as the standard towelling gown. Robes also ensure extra warmth during cold weather.
- Most people feel vulnerable when completely naked. Only expose the area being treated. During body massage, for example, don't have your client laid out like a naked corpse on the couch!
- When applying faradic pads, cover the area you have finished padding with a hand towel before you move on to the next.
- During back massage, if you think your client may feel self-conscious without her bra, place a twisted hand towel against the side of each breast.

If the tables are turned and your client insists on displaying more than you feel comfortable with, firmly insist on covering her up. Explain that, for you to finish treatment, she will need to stay covered up.

### What do you think?

1. How much do you think your physical contact and non-verbal communication affect your client's enjoyment of treatment?
2. Have you ever had an uncomfortable beauty treatment? Discuss with your colleagues what you didn't like about the treatment.

# Chapter Eleven

# Medical Conditions in the Salon

*If in doubt, consult the relevant healthcare professional.*

## Medical and pharmaceutical advances

Look out for press articles which will keep you up to date with the latest medical advances and treatments which could affect your clients. Women's magazines often cover the latest appearance-improving treatments. Leaflets with up-to-date medical advice for common skin complaints are often available free at the chemist's.

- **Hypertrichosis** can be treated with spironolactone.
- Badly sun-damaged skin can be treated with tretinoin.
- Acne and rosacea can be controlled with prescription antibiotic lotions or oral antibiotics. Over-the-counter preparations containing benzoyl peroxide and azaleic acid are also effective.
- Severe acne can be treated with isotretinoin.

## Liaising with doctors

You will need to **liaise** with your client's doctor for:

- Conditions which need medical permission for beauty treatment. For example, if an **electro-epilation** client becomes pregnant, you will need her doctor's permission to continue treatment.
- Conditions which need medical treatment. For example, if your client has a contagious skin disease such as impetigo, you cannot continue treatment until the disease is cured.
- Conditions which may need medical treatment. For example, your client's **hypertrichosis** is slow to respond to **electro-epilation**. Check that she doesn't have a hormonal imbalance, possibly due to an ovarian cyst.
- Conditions which would benefit from medical treatment. For example, during a pedicure you notice your client is beginning to develop a **hallux valgus** (bunion).

■ Preparation for medical treatment. For example, skin-softening treatments can often be useful to prepare your client's skin for plastic surgery.

## Sample doctor's letter

Type out an all-purpose doctor's referral letter. Make copies and keep them at reception. You can send the letter by post or, if you fill it out during **consultation**, you can ask your client to drop it into her surgery. (Some GPs make a small charge for a signature or letter for non-medical purposes.) Sometimes your client will need to visit her GP for examination. This may be a nuisance to your client but it is far better to inconvenience her than do her any damage.

```
                                                      Anne Other
                                                      Beauty Salon
                                                      High Street
                                                      Newtown
    Date ............................

    Re:  ............................

    Date of Birth ......... / ......... / .........


    Dear Dr ........................................,

    The above named patient has requested .................................................. treatment to

    the following area/s ..........................................................................................................

         Please indicate below if you agree to this treatment. Please inform me if this patient

    has any medical condition or takes any medication that may affect treatment.


    Yours sincerely,



       Anne Other
✄ - - - - - - - - - - - - - - - - - - - - - - - - - - - - - - - - - - - - - - - - - - - - - - - - - -

    I consent to .......................................................... receiving ................................

    treatment to the specified area/s.



    Signed ...............................................................

    Dated ...............................................................
```

**Figure 11.1**
A sample doctor's letter

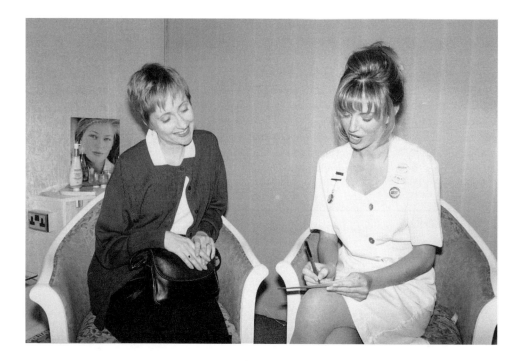

## Medical skin conditions

In the salon, you must be able to recognize **contagious** skin diseases to avoid spreading them. You also need to be able to recognize non-contagious skin conditions and to be familiar with symptoms and treatment.

## Non-contagious skin conditions

Once you have satisfied yourself the condition is non-contagious, it is important to show that you are quite happy to touch your client. As well as physical discomfort, such as soreness and itching, non-contagious skin diseases can cause sufferers severe emotional distress because the look of their skins can prompt hurtful reactions from others. Ignorance is no excuse for a professional. Common non-contagious skin conditions you should be able to recognize include:

- acne
- rosacea
- **seborrhoea** (also called seborrhoeic dermatitis)
- psoriasis
- eczema and dermatitis
- leucoderma and vitiligo
- **chloasma** (also called melasma).

If you work with sunbeds, it's also useful to know what miliaria rubra (also known as prickly heat) looks like.

> **Remember:** You aren't qualified to diagnose or treat medical skin conditions. However, you will see many faces and bodies throughout your career. If you think you spot an undiagnosed skin condition, tell your client to consult her doctor for a professional diagnosis. Write down the condition you suspect – your client could easily forget the name.

It's professional to ensure that your client has an up-to-date diagnosis and medical advice for her skin condition before you treat her.

It's tempting to try to improve diagnosed non-contagious skin conditions that haven't been helped by medication, but go carefully. Most skin conditions are very easily irritated. Use only calming and soothing treatments.

## Contagious skin conditions

Never treat clients with **contagious** skin diseases because you will spread the condition to other clients and probably yourself. Always examine the skin and nails before beginning treatment. For example, start a pedicure by wiping over both feet with a refreshing astringent – this also removes odour, which is comforting for both you and your client. As you wipe, inspect for conditions such as **tinea** or **verrucae**. Know how to recognize **contagious** skin diseases such as:

- **tinea** (ringworm/athlete's foot)
- **verrucae** (warts)
- herpes labialis (cold sore)
- conjunctivitis (pink eye)
- impetigo
- molluscum contagiosum (water wart)
- pediculosis (head lice)
- scabies (itch mite).

Find out how these conditions are treated and whether a prescription is needed for the remedy. Remember that photos of skin diseases in textbooks are generally severe, clear-cut cases. Your client's **contagious** skin condition may be mild and more difficult to spot.

## How to handle clients with **contagious** skin diseases

Assume your client hasn't noticed the condition. Surprisingly, this is often the case. Ask if what you've noticed is causing your client any problem. For example, ask, 'Are these lumps round your nail painful?' Or 'Is this nail discolouration a nuisance?' Whatever your client answers, follow up by explaining that you suspect warts around the nail or tinea unguium (fungal infection of the nail).

Avoid the word 'disease' and use the most tactful description. The medical term **tinea** sounds better than 'ringworm' or 'athlete's foot'. Advise your client that it could spread, so that she understands it's contagious. Follow this up by reassuring her there is an effective treatment available from the chemist or GP. Mention the name of the treatment and any personal experience you have of it – maybe you've used it yourself or know someone who has.

Now comes the tricky part. Your client needs to understand that you cannot treat her until the condition has cleared up. She may be feeling embarrassed and vulnerable so be careful not to make her feel worse. Alternatively, she may insist on being treated. If this happens, remain polite and discreet but firm.

> **Remember:** Never risk treating a client with a contagious skin disease. If you contract the disease you will not be able to work while you have it – warts, which are especially contagious when wet, are often resistant to treatment.

Ask your client to phone for a new appointment as soon as the condition is cleared. Ask her to let you know the outcome and tell her you'll look forward to seeing her soon. Make it clear that she can, of course, have treatment to unaffected areas.

The best outcome is that your client returns when the condition is clear, thoroughly delighted and grateful that your professional expertise and advice helped to improve the health of her skin or nails.

## Recognizing skin cancer

Spotting skin cancer is not your responsibility. However, during treatment, you will regularly see out-of-sight areas such as backs and backs of legs. Spotting the rare but sometimes fatal form, malignant melanoma, could save your client's life.

■ Basal cell epithelioma (also called basal cell carcinoma and rodent ulcer) is the least serious skin cancer. Prime sites are face and hands of mainly over-50s.

■ Squamous cell epithelioma (also called squamous cell carcinoma) appears on areas exposed to sun, mainly on the over-50s.

■ Malignant melanoma is rare but can be deadly. Prime sites are backs of legs and soles of feet – not necessarily associated with prime tanning sites or **UV** exposure. Can affect any age and kill quickly. See Winyard (1996) *A guide for health and beauty therapists* Addison Wesley Longman.

■ About 20 per cent of keratoses – warty overgrowths due to UV exposure – turn into skin cancer.

**Figure 11.3**
Incidence of skin cancer

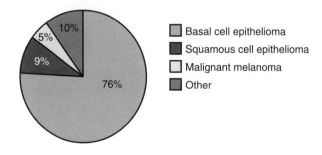

If you suspect skin cancer, don't alarm your client with the word 'cancer' unless you suspect malignant melanoma, but send her straight to her GP with an urgent note to check out her 'skin lesion'.

## Health and diet

Give only sound diet advice, promote a healthy body image and encourage sensible diet management. Discourage crash dieting. After the first week, to avoid burning muscle rather than fat, your clients should lose no more than 1kg (2lb) per week. Likewise, discourage appetite suppressants (slimming pills), diet myths and faddy diets. If need be, refer your client to a dietician or nutritionist.

Eating disorders are commonest in women but can also affect men. They include:

■ anorexia nervosa

■ bulimia nervosa

■ compulsive eating disorder.

Anorexia nervosa is often called 'the slimmer's disease' but this is a misleading name. It's not simply dieting which has got out of hand. It's not vanity that makes young girls starve themselves, sometimes to death. Anorexics use self-inflicted starvation as a way of gaining self-esteem and control over their emotional and psychological problems or the pressures of growing up. Anorexia isn't so much linked to the pressures of advertising but more to the stresses of teenage life.

If body weight falls below a Body Mass Index (BMI) of around 17.5 **menstruation** can stop (**amenorrhoea**). Lack of female hormones can lead to growth of **lanugo** hair all over the body and thin, dry skin and hair. Some anorexics don't admit to their condition. Some are genuinely unaware of it.

Bulimics are only too aware of their condition because bulimia involves bingeing on food and vomiting it back up or passing it out using laxatives. Compulsive eaters also binge but do not purge so they are easier to spot since they rapidly become **obese**. GPs may or may not know their patients have eating disorders.

If you suspect your client has an undiagnosed eating disorder, try to establish this tactfully. Don't mistake naturally slender people for anorexics. Some people are perfectly healthy but thin. If you think your client is anorexic, mention that you suspect she may be underweight for her height and ask if you may work out her BMI. Always refer clients with undiagnosed eating disorders to their GPs. It's very unlikely that anorexics will go, so also provide the telephone number of a local self-help group.

You can still treat clients with eating disorders, so long as you encourage healthy eating and weight control or gain as appropriate. Be honest about how thin your anorexic client is, but at the same time try to encourage her to feel positive about herself and boost her confidence. Timely advice from a professional such as you can steer a vulnerable girl away from developing an eating disorder which will blight her life.

> **Remember:** Other medical conditions which can affect weight and diet are:
> ■ diabetes mellitus
> ■ thyroid imbalances.

> **Remember:** The Body Mass Index (BMI) is more accurate than weight charts for establishing if your client has a healthy body weight:
>
> weight in kilograms ÷ (height in metres$^2$)
>
> (Multiply height in metres by itself, then divide weight in kilograms by this number.)
>
> - 20 to 24 is considered healthy for women.
> - 20 to 25 is considered healthy for men.
> - 25 to 30 is considered overweight.
> - Over 30 is considered obese.
>
> Below 17.5 is considered underweight (anorexia may be the cause).

## Excess hair

As you begin training, you will notice that women are hairier than society generally believes them to be. 'Excess' body or facial hair growth is often inherited and can be normal for some women. Occasionally, excessive hair growth is caused by disease, usually involving androgen-producing **endocrine** glands such as the ovaries. Hair growth then follows the male hair-growth pattern.

These terms are used to describe hair growth.

- **Hirsutism** is excessive 'abnormal' hair growth in women, generally following the male pattern, possibly caused by disease involving **endocrine** glands. A woman with a full beard growth is **hirsute**.
- **Hypertrichosis** (also called 'idiopathic' or 'constitutional' hirsutism) is excessive hair growth which is normal for that person, possibly due to heredity or sensitivity to medication rather than disease. A woman with very hairy forearms or calves is **hypertrichotic**.
- **Superfluous hair** is any growth of hair which is 'normal' but unwanted.

If your client is excessively hairy and her menstrual cycle is irregular (or longer than 35 days), suggest she ask her GP to test her hormone levels. It is rare for a hormonal imbalance to be found but this may simply mean that tests are not yet sensitive enough to pick up slight imbalances.

Women with 'normal' hormone levels can still have coarse, terminal hair:

- on the back of the thigh
- down the inner thigh
- on the big toe
- from the bikini line to the navel
- over the lower half of the abdomen
- around the nipple
- along the midline of the chest.

Many women find excess body hair distressing. Reassure your client that body hair is quite natural and normal in women. Indeed, it is to be expected during the **menopause**. Excessive but 'normal' hair growth can be medically treated with anti-androgen drugs (spironolactone) from the GP as well as by **electro-epilation**. Early treatment is best since once hairs are stimulated to coarsen, this cannot be reversed.

Coarse, **terminal hair** on the back or shoulders of women is generally an indication of hormonal imbalance or disease. Refer your client to her GP. Of course, diseases whose symptoms include **hirsutism** need medical treatment before electro-epilation can be effective:

- chronic anovulation, e.g. polycystic ovarian syndrome (PCOS), Stein-Leventhal syndrome
- pituitary or adrenal tumour, e.g. acromegaly, Cushing's syndrome
- adrenogenital syndrome
- Archard-Thiers syndrome
- Addison's disease.

Sparse hair conditions may indicate:

- thyroid disorders
- Frohlich's syndrome
- Simmond's syndrome.

# Common medical conditions

During **consultation**, some clients will tell you they have a medical condition or take medication. Don't be afraid to ask questions to find out how your client's health is affected by the condition or medication. Keep an up-to-date medical encyclopaedia in your salon to check up on unfamiliar conditions. If you're not sure whether treatment is **indicated**, don't take your client's word for it: always check with her doctor first.

## Diabetes

Some beauty treatments are **contra-indicated** to clients with diabetes. This is because they can suffer from:

- neuropathy (nerve damage) which means they cannot feel injury or extreme hot or cold
- ischaemia (restricted blood supply) which means they are prone to infection, which is often slow to heal.

Many diabetic clients can be treated with their GP's permission. Take care not to cut, scratch or graze your diabetic client's skin. It is especially important not to cut or tear skin on the foot or toes, where circulation is poorest. Trim toe-nails straight across with clippers. Never cut cuticles or poke under the nail plate. Untreated foot infections in diabetic clients can cause very serious health problems. Tell your diabetic client if you notice any infection, inflammation or discharge on her feet.

If treatment involves skin-piercing, for example, **electro-epilation**, carefully monitor intensity and frequency of treatment and keep a close eye on skin healing.

## Epilepsy

A number of beauty treatments – particularly electrical ones – are **contra-indicated** for clients with epilepsy. This is because electrical currents – especially **high frequency** – can trigger attacks. However, epileptic clients whose condition is well controlled by medication can often have treatment, providing their doctors' permission is gained. The following aromatherapy oils are **contra-indicated** for epileptic clients since they trigger an attack: rosemary, sage, wormwood, hyssop and fennel.

## Arthritis

Clients with arthritis have painful, stiff joints with limited movement. The affected joints, particularly the joints in the hands and feet may look red, swollen and distorted.

- Osteoarthritis attacks the joints and can be due to wear and tear. It affects many over-50s.
- Rheumatoid arthritis attacks joints and muscles and can affect anyone at any age.

Handle clients with arthritis gently. Heat treatments are soothing. Take particular care not to cause discomfort when performing passive movements during massage.

**Figure 11.4** Paraffin wax treatment is soothing for arthritic conditions

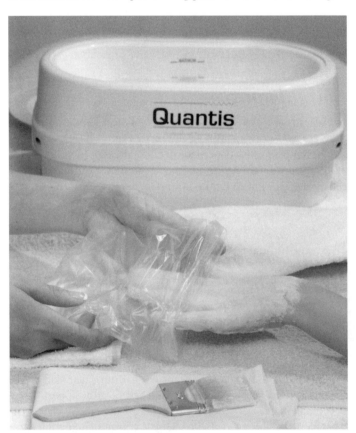

### What do you think?

1. A client who appears to be anorexic books a course of electronic muscle stimulation. Do you agree to treat her?
2. Although it is comparatively rare, why is it important for electrologists to be able to spot signs that excess hair growth may be caused by disease?

# Chapter Twelve

# Different Types of Client

*Make each client feel welcome and valued.*

## Regular clients

Don't take your regular clients for granted. Regular clients deserve special status because they guarantee your main income. Ensure they get first choice of appointments at busy times such as Christmas. If your client records are on computer, set up a system to send newsletters, Christmas or birthday cards to make your regular clients feel special. (However, don't annoy clients with too much direct mail.)

## Invite clients to become regulars

Offer to reserve appointments for clients who book regularly. Your client need ring only if she needs to cancel. Explain that as a regular client, she will get priority booking. Be sure you make a careful note of regular clients' appointments and copy them straight into the new appointment book when it is made up.

## Regular clients as models

When work experience students visit salons, they often sit around watching salon staff rush about. If the trainee is competent – with her agreement – invite regular clients to book relaxing low-risk treatments such a manicure, pedicure, basic facials, make-up and body massage with the trainee. **Electro-epilation** clients often look forward to this as a treat.

Clients may not value completely free treatment, so charge a pound or two and give this to the trainee. Alternatively, suggest the client tip what she thinks appropriate.

With this system of work experience, regular clients are introduced to new treatments, trainees gain valuable experience plus a little pocket money and staff are free to attend to paying clients.

## Male clients

Today's society encourages men to be well groomed – and quite right too! Most women encourage the use of male fragrance such as aftershave. Male skin care ranges are well established. Ranges of male nail polish and waxing products are growing in popularity. Modern men care very much about their appearance. Many book salon treatments for the same reason many women do – to make themselves look attractive.

## How to treat male clients

Male beauty salon clients are no scarier than male hairdressing clients are. If you have never treated a man before, act as if you do it every day and he may become a regular client. If you show suspicion, disapproval or embarrassment, he will never return.

- Emphasize the 'health' aspect of the treatment. Avoid using the word 'beauty'.
- Don't expect a man to put on a pink bathrobe; use appropriately coloured towels and blankets.
- Ensure all treatments offered to men are suitable. Think them through beforehand to avoid embarrassment. For example, protect his hairline from products with a length of crêpe bandage which looks more clinical than a headband.

**Figure 12.1**
Depilatory wax targeted specifically at a male clientele

## Waxing

Men book waxing for practical reasons. Some suppliers market waxing products designed specifcally for male clients. Male models, dancers, body builders and weightlifters wax to improve appearance; swimmers wax to improve performance in the water; cyclists wax for safety – greased, hair-free legs are less likely to graze.

- Men are generally hairier than women are. For a comfortable wax, expect to use more fabric strips per treatment.
- Trim long hair with round-bladed scissors before waxing – this cuts down 'pull' and makes treatment more comfortable.

- When waxing an unfamiliar area such as the chest, remember to study the direction of the hair growth before applying the wax. This will tell you the direction in which to remove the strip.

Areas men have waxed include:

- Between the eyebrows. Tidy stray hairs below the brows if required – but don't shape!
- Back and shoulders. Male-pattern baldness is often accompanied by increased hair growth on shoulders and back. Some men feel this is unattractive. Hair growth changes direction below the waist. Wax either side of the spine in manageable strips. The finished result should look as natural as possible, so offer to wax noticeable terminal hair on shoulders, neck and upper arms if necessary.
- Chest. Hair growth changes direction at the top of the sternum. Wax either side of the mid-line, one side at a time in small, manageable sections. Leave a few hairs round the nipple – don't wax over it!
- Legs. The hair growth pattern is the same on both sexes.

## *Manicure*

Some men are comfortable using cosmetics traditionally associated with women and others aren't. It also depends on the current fashion. There are no hard and fast rules about offering polish.

- File men's fingernails straight across, like toenails.
- Concentrate on cuticle work.
- Use an unperfumed 'massage medium' rather than 'hand cream' for the hand and arm massage.
- Finish treatment by buffing to a healthy shine using a leather nail buffer. If he wants polish, he'll ask.

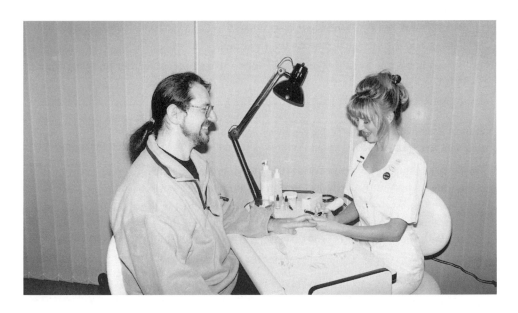

**Figure 12.2**
Cuticle work on a
male manicure
client

## Facials

Use a male skin care range if possible. If you don't have one, avoid strongly perfumed products – your sensitive skin care range should be suitable. Favour 'simple' preparations such as witch hazel and clay masks. Many men are grateful for skin analysis and practical skin care advice.

- Unless your client is very closely shaved, use large, flat cosmetic sponges in place of cotton wool pads since these catch on beard growth or stubble.
- Concentrate on **comedone** extraction.
- The skin beneath beards and 'designer stubble' benefits greatly from exfoliation.
- Don't apply face mask to moustache or full beard growth; it's difficult to clean off.
- Most men welcome eyebrow tidies, but remember not to shape.

## Ear-piercing

Be sure to pierce a male client's *left* ear unless he requests otherwise. Traditionally, homosexual men have the *right* ear pierced. If your client asks you to pierce his right ear, check tactfully if he knows about the tradition first, especially if he is a youngster.

## Body massage

If you prefer not to perform massage on male clients, tell your employer when you start work. A good employer will respect your decision.

---

**Remember:** As a professional, you are entitled to professional respect. Provocative or flirtatious behaviour is always inappropriate between a professional and client. If your client's behaviour embarrasses you or makes you feel uncomfortable:

- Stop physical contact.
- Explain that you have to stop treatment because of his unacceptable behaviour. Ask him to come to reception when he is dressed.
- Charge him the standard rate for the treatment.
- Politely but firmly explain that you will not be able to accept further bookings from him.

---

Ask male massage clients to bring a pair of loose shorts to wear during treatment. This avoids confusion or embarrassment about what to take off.

- Keep a pair of large, drawstring shorts at reception for this purpose. (Any garment lent to a client must be laundered between treatments.)
- Shorts keep the male client's erogenous zone (the area sensitive to sexual stimulus) covered. On male clients, the erogenous zone begins below the **umbilicus** and extends down the inner thigh to a few inches above the knee. The buttocks are included; the lower half of the outer thigh is not. In other words, avoid all contact with his inner thigh, lower abdomen and the area covered by his shorts!

- It is acceptable to treat naked male residents in a health farm setting.
- On **hirsute** clients, replace the usual massage medium of oil with talcum powder to avoid 'pull' on hairs.
- Use a deeper massage technique on men because they have a larger percentage of muscle than women have.
- The basic massage routine is the same with the addition of pétrissage to the **pectoral** muscles.

### Transvestite clients

Transvestite means 'cross-dresser'. Male transvestites like to wear clothes and make-up traditionally associated with women. They can be heterosexual, homosexual or bisexual. Treat a transvestite client the same as a male client. Refer to him as 'Mr' or 'he'.

## Children

A beauty salon is not a suitable place for young children for the following reasons:

- They risk accident from hazards the mother may not notice, such as wax heaters, spa pools and hazardous chemicals.
- They need careful and constant supervision.
- Their presence makes it impossible for their mother to relax completely.
- They need amusement.
- They can disturb other clients – this is equally true of therapists' own children.

If an accident happens, it will be considered your fault. Check your public liability insurance policy to see if children are insured to enter your salon.

### Clients' children

Sometimes clients turn up with young children. If insurance allows, accept them graciously but explain that, for safety reasons, it's best if they don't accompany your client next time.

> **Remember:** When children are in the salon, your first priority is no longer your client. It is to keep the child safe at all times.

Sleeping babies must be placed in a *safe* and *secure* place. Use your own judgement and move the baby if the mother places him somewhere unsafe such as under the couch or near the waxer.

Do your best to amuse children. It's not good practice to give children salon equipment such as cosmetic brushes to play with. An all-purpose toy, book or game kept at reception can be a lifesaver during school holidays.

> **Remember:** Keep toys or books in good order and as clean as the rest of the salon equipment. Mother will notice this.

## Child clients

Sometimes children themselves are clients. A person under 18 is legally termed a **minor**. Children can have beauty treatments but first check that your insurance policy covers **minors** and use your professional judgement to advise the parent whether treatment is appropriate.

- The only treatment suitable for a pre-teen child – who should be accompanied by an adult – is a manicure. Manicures can encourage some children to stop biting their nails.
- A teenager under 16 may have a make-up lesson or a facial with skin care advice.
- Waxing or bleaching of superfluous hair is suitable for a teenager under 16 providing she is accompanied by an adult – at least for the first session – and willing to have the treatment.
- Slimming treatments are not appropriate for children under 16 but healthy eating advice is fine.
- Children under 16 may not have **electro-epilation**. A client aged 17 must have permission from her doctor.
- Don't allow children under 16 to use sunbeds or have **UV** treatment.
- Even if a treatment is **contra-indicated** to a **minor**, provided you don't perform treatment, you can still book a **consultation** to advise or reassure your young client about her concerns.

### Ear-piercing and **minors**

- Unaccompanied ear-piercing clients under 18 must have written permission from a parent or guardian.
- If parents bring **minors** for ear-piercing, advise that the child must be mature enough to understand and accept some discomfort. The child must also be responsible enough to perform the aftercare routine for at least 6 weeks; recognize symptoms of infection and avoid injury to the ear lobe during play. There are no clear-cut legal requirements, but you may like to advise the parent to wait until the child is at least 12 years old.
- Piercing babies' ears is best discouraged since it causes unnecessary trauma for baby, parent and therapist. You'll have no difficulty piercing the first ear but once the baby realizes this hurts, sensibly she'll struggle to avoid having the second ear hurt. It's unprofessional to leave your client half-treated but it's unethical to treat a distressed client. It's difficult to pierce the second ear accurately. The parent may even need to restrain the baby physically for you to be able to finish the treatment. As you can see, this is a bad state of affairs for everyone. If the parent continues to insist, explain that babies' earlobes grow and the pierce may finish up too low on her adult lobe. If you prefer not to pierce babies' ears, politely explain this to your employer who should respect your decision.

> **Remember:** If your child client is unwilling to have treatment, such as waxing or ear-piercing, advise the parent politely that it won't be possible for you to perform the treatment. If necessary, explain that this is because the treatment will cause the child unnecessary emotional trauma. (If parents insist on treatment to an unwilling child, they could, theoretically, be open to prosecution for cruelty.)

# Clients with particular needs

## Mature clients

The **menopause** begins between 40 and 55 when women gradually stop having monthly periods. Women sometimes suffer sudden hot flushes and sweats which some find embarrassing. Excess facial hair growth during the **menopause** is common.

Some **menopausal** women choose to have HRT (hormone replacement therapy) to remedy symptoms. Extra female hormones are delivered into the skin through a 'matrix patch'. Matrix patches look very similar to large round sticking plasters or Clingfilm patches. They are usually stuck around the hip area. Try not to disturb them but if you loosen one during treatment, mention it to your client. She will need to apply a fresh one when she gets home.

After the **menopause**, skin often becomes less elastic and drier and hair and nails become more brittle because there are fewer female hormones. In both men and women, ageing skin is also affected by a reduction in:

- blood flow
- subcutaneous fat
- sebaceous secretions
- functioning **melanocytes**
- water content.

## Physically disabled clients

It is illegal under the Disability Discrimination Act 1995 to treat disabled clients differently from able-bodied clients just because of their disability. It would indeed be mean to refuse a disabled client treatment because you think it may be a bit inconvenient for you. Accommodate disabled clients as best you can. The only acceptable reason for refusal is because of health and safety concerns.

If you need to lift your disabled client, remember to put safety first for yourself and your client. She won't want you to put your physical health at risk by lifting her alone, so always be sure to ask a colleague for help. Remember that there is a great difference between physical and mental disability. After taking her physical limitations into account, treat your physically disabled client just the same as any other client.

Use your everyday speech. There's no need to avoid certain words or phrases connected with your client's disability. It's fine to say to a blind client, 'See you next week'.

## Clients with physical disfigurements

A client who looks different may take you by surprise at first but remember to treat her like the normal person she is. Make sufficient eye contact as you talk to her. As your client talks, you will soon get to know her and no longer see her as 'different'. Only ask about the disfigurement if it is relevant to treatment. Your client will discuss it with you when and if she wants to – it can be tedious to be quizzed about physical **anomalies**.

## Transsexual clients

Transsexuals sometimes visit beauty salons. They look like ordinary women or like men dressed as women. Transsexual means 'crossing over to the opposite sex'. A transsexual man is sexually attracted to men and has either become a woman after having a sex change operation – substituting a vagina for a penis – or is preparing for sex change by living as a woman.

Treat a transsexual client as a female client. If she has had a sex change operation, she is female. Refer to her as 'Miss' or 'she'. Beauty therapists can be of great support to transsexual clients, who often need help with female **deportment**, superfluous hair removal and **electro-epilation** or camouflage cosmetics to remove or disguise beard growth. Changing sex is traumatic. Do your best to make your client feel relaxed and accepted and treat her like any other woman.

## Bridal clients

Offer your bridal client a specialized free **consultation** and discuss how treatments can help her prepare for her special day. Make her feel special by devising something like a 'Wine and Roses Bridal Package'. For example, place a red rose in the treatment room and offer sparkling wine.

On the wedding day, timing is vital. Give your bridal party priority over other clients, who will generally understand. Each wedding is an unrepeatable and stressful event. Do your best to make it memorable for the right reasons. You can make a big contribution to the success of the day by keeping your bride in good humour, relaxed and reassured.

- Straggly brows and flaky skin cannot be disguised by even the best bridal make-up. Advise a facial or course of facials and an eyebrow shape or tidy a week beforehand.

- Redness and swelling from eyebrow tweezing is difficult to disguise with make-up, which may also introduce infection into the empty follicles. Advise your client to book treatment which results in **erythema** or **oedema** a few days before the wedding day.

- Always advise a trial-run bridal make-up so that there is no indecision – from you or your bride – on the day.

- Choose your bride's colour cosmetics to tone with the colour of her bridesmaid's dresses and flowers.

- Apply an anti-shine photographic make-up, particularly if the wedding is to be videoed.

- Brides are generally videoed or photographed signing the register. Suggest a manicure or course of manicures. Recommend a conditioning treatment if needed.

- Since nail polish can take up to one hour to dry completely, book the manicure the previous evening. Explain that you can repair chipped polish the following morning during the make-up appointment.

---

**Why not build up a bridal make-up portfolio?** Ask your brides for a portrait shot – offer to pay – most brides will be so pleased with their make-up they'll give you a photo. Studying these photos is also a useful way to ensure your photographic make-up technique is effective.

---

- Brides are often nervous. Don't keep your client waiting and don't seem unsure about anything – particularly if something goes wrong.

- If you need to cancel an appointment connected with a wedding, always speak to your client personally. A message may never reach her.

## Pregnant clients

> **Remember:** Safety first for your pregnant client's unborn baby. If treatment isn't considered completely safe for the baby, it's **contra-indicated** during pregnancy.

Some aromatherapy oils such as lavender, camomile and peppermint are **contra-indicated** for the first few months of pregnancy because they are thought to bring on menstruation. Don't apply aromatherapy oils to the abdomen of a pregnant client without her doctor's permission.

- Don't use **toxic** oils (see page 12) on pregnant clients. It's also wise to avoid basil, bay, clary sage, camphor, fennel, hyssop, juniper, marjoram, melissa, myrrh, parsley, rosemary, tarragon and thyme.
- Some treatments such as **electro-epilation** need written permission from your client's GP. If you are not sure if treatment is **indicated**, always contact your client's doctor beforehand.

The second consideration for pregnant clients is comfort.

- Pregnant women, particularly when heavily pregnant, cannot lie on their stomachs. During leg waxing, ask your client to lie on her side with her top leg crooked. Wax both legs as far round the back as you can. Then ask your client to switch sides and continue waxing. Finally, adjust the couch to a sitting position while you wax the narrow strip of hair remaining down the front of her legs. When your client is standing, double-check that the backs of her legs are hair-free.
- Perform back and neck massage with your client propped against a couple of large pillows or sitting astride a chair, leaning her head and arms on a pillow folded over the chair back. Women find it uncomfortable to lie flat on their backs in advanced pregnancy.

## Celebrity clients

A true professional treats every client like a celebrity, but when you treat a celebrity or titled client, your first consideration is discretion and confidentiality. Never reveal any information about a celebrity client to anyone in any form.

There is no need to feel nervous when performing treatments on celebrities. They are people, just like you. Pamper them, but don't go over the top and don't ask for autographs or act 'star-struck'. While initially flattering, this behaviour will quickly become annoying to your celebrity client, who simply wants to relax.

## Clients who act strangely

Mental imbalances can affect anyone at any time. Understandably, clients who act in an unexpected way can seem alarming.

- 'Neurosis' is the term used to describe everyday mental anxiety. For example, your client may tell you she has claustrophobia or panic attacks.

- ■ 'Psychosis' is a more severe type of mental illness that must be treated with regular medication.

- ■ A client who is highly agitated and excited may be in the manic phase of a bipolar condition (formerly known as manic depression).

- ■ A client who seems to be listening or talking to someone imaginary may be schizophrenic.

- ■ An older client who continually repeats herself or makes odd claims may have Alzheimer's disease (presenile dementia).

Clients showing signs of psychosis aren't generally a threat. Treat them as you would any other client but bear in mind that during psychotic episodes, they see the world in a different way and may be unreliable or quickly become irrational or unpredictable.

## Challenging clients

Working with people can be very rewarding and occasionally stressful. Most people are a bundle of vulnerabilities and insecurities. Deal kindly with stressful clients and remember that they can only stress you if you let them. Always act professionally and stay in control of the situation at all times.

> **Remember:** People will take up as much time as you let them. Fob watches are useful for checking the time discreetly. If you wear a wristwatch, wear the face on your inner wrist so you can glance at it less noticeably.

## Challenging clients: Questions and Answers

**1. Q** *How can I take my leave of a chatty client without seeming rude?*

**A** Wait for a pause in conversation after treatment then offer to book her next appointment while she dresses. This will give you a few minutes to show your next client to the treatment room – or to a seat outside it. While this client gets undressed, meet the first client at reception. She won't want to continue the conversation by then.

   If you have a particularly talkative client, try using her name to distract her from what she is saying to what you are saying.

**2. Q** *How do I tactfully move one client from the manicure station to make way for the next?*

**A** Introduce your first client to the waiting client. She will then realize her appointment has ended and she won't want to take up the next client's time. This also reassures the next client that she will not have long to wait.

**3. Q** *There's one client I dread. She's never satisfied and wants all my time and attention.*

**A** Most salons have one or two 'heart sink' clients. An unreasonably demanding client can be a drain on your time and energy. Try to stay relaxed and polite but be firm and keep control of the situation so that she respects you as a professional. If your professionalism doesn't suit her, let her try her luck elsewhere.

**4. Q** *Now and again my client forgets an appointment.*

**A** From time to time, clients arrive late or miss appointments. If this happens regularly, give her a 'courtesy call'. Ring – or ask your receptionist to ring – her the day before the appointment with a simple messages such as 'May I confirm your facial appointment for tomorrow at four?' The courtesy call is of course, an extra service for 'busy' clients, not a rude reminder!

**5. Q** *My client skips several appointments at a time. This is trying my patience and losing the salon money.*

**A** By law you may charge a **cancellation fee** – the cost or half the cost of treatment – for a broken appointment. It is often more economical to deter habitual appointment skippers from making further appointments. Explain politely that no more appointments should be booked until the debt is settled. The aim is to put the client off rebooking but clients sometimes choose to pay the fee. Either way the problem is solved.

**6. Q** *My client is* always *late and this throws out all my following appointments.*

**A** Treat the habitual latecomer with her remaining appointment time only, even if a free appointment or your lunch break follows. She will soon realize she'll do better to arrive on time.

# Chapter Thirteen

# Ethical Selling

*If your client isn't best served, your salon isn't best served.*

## Why salons sell

In beauty salons and other **service industries**, profit is made on services provided by workers. Workers are expensive. This means that 'labour-intensive' industries such as **service industries**, can find it hard to make a good profit. If your salon is not profitable, before long, you will have no salon.

This is why many salons not only provide services but also sell retail products. At least a third of salon profit should come from retail sales.

> **Remember:** It's tempting to stock related products such as jewellery, lingerie or swimwear in your salon. This can work, but be wary of markets you don't know. Your clients may be happy to buy their cosmetics from you, but not their swimwear.

## Why clients buy

All moisturizers are basically oil-in-water emulsions. Some dermatologists suggest simply using the cheapest or even petroleum jelly. Both will prevent water evaporating from skin but how pleasant are they to use? Price is not always the first consideration when choosing a daily moisturizer – you have to look forward to using it! Many other factors can also influence your client's choice of moisturizer.

- Packaging – your client may be attracted to either simple or elaborate packaging.
- Texture – she may favour a rich or light texture.
- Smell – if a cream smells unpleasant, your client won't use it, however beneficial it is.
- Ingredients – your client may avoid certain ingredients she is sensitive to. She may favour certain ingredients such as sun block.
- Brand image – your client may feel a brand name guarantees quality or she may feel she is paying extra for the company's advertising costs.

You won't be able to please every client with your choice of retail product. Make your product choice only after thorough and careful market research. Always test products on yourself and your colleagues to see if they really live up to manufacturers' claims, which are sometimes exaggerated.

## Make stock easy to buy

Make buying your salon's products as easy as possible for your client. Products that are displayed in reception often sell themselves, particularly if testers look inviting.

- Price individual products clearly and correctly. No one likes having to ask the price. Some clients assume that unpriced products are expensive. Clear pricing also helps the seller avoid mistakes.
- Encourage clients who haven't had treatment with the products to try out the testers.

**Figure 13.1**
Encourage clients
to try out testers

- Tell clients about products you've used and liked.
- Whenever you apply cosmetics to a client, always note down the shades on her **record card**. At some stage, she may wish to buy them.

### Out of stock

Running out of stock is annoying for your client and bad business for your salon. If it happens:

- Offer to take your client's name and number and tell her you will telephone her when the product arrives.

- Give her an idea of how long the product will take to arrive.
- Make sure the product is on order.
- Reserve it for your client as soon as it arrives.
- Don't forget to ring!

Always put client service before salon sales. If you don't stock the product your client needs, don't talk her into something less suitable. Suggest where she can get the product.

### Keep stock hygienic

Remember to apply hygiene rules to retail stock and testers. Never allow a client to test a retail product.

- All retail products must be uncontaminated and kept in perfect condition. Ideally, retail cosmetics and creams should have a tamper-proof seal but until that happens, stick a small square of sticky tape over the box, bottle or tube. This will prevent clients trying to test retail stock.
- Encourage clients to test cosmetics before they buy. If this prevents a sale, then clearly the product was not suitable in the first place. A tester should be provided for this purpose alone. If no tester is available, hygienically remove some cream or cosmetic from the salon pot with a clean spatula in the same way as you would during treatment.
- The set of cosmetics used during make-up treatment should not double as testers for your clients to try. This practice contaminates the cosmetics and risks **cross-infection**.

## Serving versus selling

Some therapists find it difficult to be both server and seller at the same time. Should you sell for the salon or serve the client? If you always give your client the best possible service, there isn't a conflict of interests. In a modern salon, your client will expect selling as part of the service.

If you find that you enjoy helping or advising your client regardless of whether you sell her something, then you are a true professional. Always be honest about treatments and what they can do. Selling techniques can be helpful, but if you don't feel comfortable with them, neither will your client.

### Money

Value for money has different meanings to different people. Some may consider body wraps to gain temporary inch loss a waste of money, but if it gets you into your wedding dress it's worth every penny!

Practically everyone who visits a beauty salon has some **disposable income**. There's no need to feel bad about parting your client from her cash. Unless your powers of persuasion are legendary, your clients won't buy what they don't want. Never apologize for the price of a product or service. Give your client your best advice, then do her the courtesy of leaving her to judge how she wants to spend her money.

You may recommend a facial once a month but if your client wants one every week then, so long as it does her no harm, this is fine. However, never be talked into performing unnecessary treatment – for example, don't epilate blonde, **vellus** facial hair when it's clearly not necessary.

## What does your client like or lack?

During treatment, ask your client about her skin and her skin care routine. Listen to what she tells you. Ask about her skin care products. (You can also gauge her budget from this.) Find out what she wants and needs from her skin care and cosmetic range. Is she dissatisfied with anything? Explain to her how your product can make a specific improvement such as combating dryness.

> **Remember:**   You have two ears and one mouth. Successful selling is largely about listening.

# Can it be unprofessional not to sell?

Clients come to salons to find out about the latest cosmetic and skin care advances. Young clients especially enjoy hearing about these.

- Don't be mean with your professional expertise. You'd recommend using professional emery boards to a friend, wouldn't you? Why not sell them to your clients?
- It's more professional to advise your client to book a course rather than a single treatment, which will have little effect.
- If your facial client has lots of **comedones** or **milia** to remove, it's more professional to advise her to book a course of facials rather than remove all the blockages in one treatment and risk causing her discomfort or worse, skin damage.

## Products your clients need

Your client may think you are unprofessional – even annoying – if you don't offer to sell her the product she needs. Don't leave her to hunt round chemists for inferior products; you have a good-quality product to hand, along with expertise on how to use it correctly! Your treatment-related products should practically sell themselves.

- A nail extension client will need a good quality non-acetone nail polish remover.
- A waxing client will need effective antiseptic aftercare lotion.
- An ear-piercing client will need appropriate antiseptic aftercare solution. Surgical spirit is not recommended since it dehydrates healing skin.
- A client with newly applied individual lashes will need an oil-free eye-make-up remover.
- Eyelash tint clients will be interested to try clear gel mascara.
- A client who books her first nail extensions may like to get used to longer nails by wearing stick-on ones in the meantime.
- Clients who book a course of sunbed treatments will need specialized UV tanning cream.

- Always suggest your client books a heat treatment before her massage, since this will make the treatment more effective. (The exception is aromatherapy, when it's **contra-indicated**.)
- Your bridal client will practically insist you sell her the lipstick you chose for her make-up.
- A client who buys a lipstick will almost certainly be interested to see the matching nail polish.
- The tiny brush sold with blusher compacts is unsuitable for application. Offer a fat, long-handled blusher brush for your client to buy.

## Selling dos and don'ts

Selling techniques exist to help you; don't become a slave to them. Always put your client's welfare above selling a product or treatment and you won't go wrong.

### Use your expertise

Clients will ask your advice because *you* are the expert. Become an expert on your salon's products and cosmetics and know how to use them correctly. Learn about ingredients, what they do, what they don't do and how they work. Ideally, use the salon ranges yourself. Hopefully, your salon provides staff with products at cost price.

Examples of expertise which can help you sell products include:

**Figure 13.2**
Leaflets inform clients and promote treatment

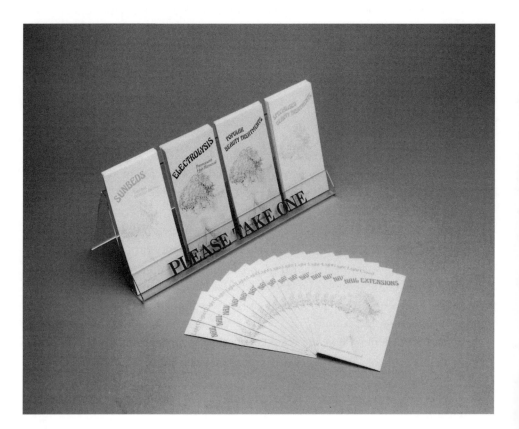

- Advising on **UVB** and **UVA** sun protection.
- Flaky skin is always a sign of dry or dehydrated skin which needs a moisturizer.
- Most moisturizing creams are too heavy for the delicate skin of the eye area. If your client complains of puffiness around the eyes, she needs a specialized eye cream.
- Apply some colour cosmetics – facial cosmetics are not recommended – after a facial treatment, especially if your client arrived fully made-up. This is a good way to introduce your facial client to your range of cosmetics.

Examples of expertise which can help you sell services include:

- If your bride is having her wedding videoed, her make-up should be natural colours with no hard lines. Hard kohl lines can cause colours to 'flare' in close-up.
- Your client will be keen to buy products and cosmetics when accompanied with 'tricks of the trade' tips on how to use them to best advantage. For example, white kajal pencil applied to the inner eye rim is a favourite with photographic models and can work well for brides.
- One make-up lesson can soon pay for itself in savings on unsuitable colour cosmetics.
- Depilatory cream is not recommended for facial skin. Its active ingredient, calcium thioglycollate is similar to a weak perm lotion and can cause a chemical burn on sensitive skin. Advise an alternative method of dealing with facial hair.

## How to sell

Never assume that your client knows what you know. Always explain why you recommend a particular product or treatment for her. Your client will be very interested to learn exactly what she can expect of it.

**Figure 13.3**
'Ear piercing, no appointment necessary' is a preferable alternative to this commonly seen invitation

Salon posters, leaflets and information sheets are useful because they serve two functions:

- They provide your client with information
- They help promote treatment and products.

**Figure 13.4**
Become an expert
on your skin care
range

> **Remember:**   Your client is only interested in how your product can help her, she's
> not interested in a general overview of your entire range.

Everyone is inspired by enthusiasm. If your product is brilliant at covering under-eye shadows, say so. Don't say it's 'quite good'. Tell your client how brilliant it is – she'll enjoy using it all the more.

Likewise, if the shade of lipstick you're applying to your client's lips really suits her, don't keep it to yourself – tell her how terrific it looks!

## When not to sell

*Listen* to what your client tells you and *watch* her **body language**. If you read your client's **body language** carefully, you will soon learn when to pursue a sale and when to back off.

- Learn to tell when a client prefers to browse alone and when she wants your help and advice.
- Never sell your client a treatment or product which could harm her. For example, never sell a client who won't tan a course of sunbed treatments.
- Never sell your client a treatment or product which won't benefit her. For example, don't sell your client a course of **electro-epilation** when bleaching is more appropriate.
- Don't bombard your new client with all the benefits, ingredients and prices of your entire range. Your client may assume you put sales before service, feel pressurized and never return.
- Don't plug your products while your client is trying to relax during a massage or face mask.

## How not to sell

You're not selling timeshare apartments. No matter what advice your **rep** gives you, don't subject your client to lengthy sales patter or pressure her into buying.

■ If you persuade her to buy something she doesn't want or can't afford, using 'the hard sell', she'll leave your salon with 'buyer's remorse' regretting her purchase. She'll then develop a bad feeling about you and your salon and never return.

■ Never use **misinformation** to help you sell. This is information that sounds convincing but isn't true. When you have technical expertise it is easy to use **misinformation** to sell, but don't be tempted. This is grossly unprofessional. One day, one of your clients will catch you out and your credibility will be ruined.

■ It's unethical to take advantage of clients' vulnerabilities. For example, clients who suffer from conditions such as acne or hair loss can become desperate to find a 'cure'. It is only too easy to sell to desperate clients. First, help these clients gain the latest medical advice, then and only then, sell them your products *if* they really are effective.

### Quiz – Are you an ethical salesperson?

1. *Mrs G asks you to advise her on the best shade of mascara for her colouring. She is very fair and you decide that the best shade is brown. Your salon range only provides black. Do you:*
   a) Suggest where she may buy a more suitable brown mascara?
   b) Sell her a black mascara because you need the commission?
   c) Say you're not really sure and ask her to come back on Wednesday (your day off)?

2. *Miss P has chosen a product that includes lanolin. You know from a previous consultation that she is sensitive to lanolin. Do you:*
   a) Ask if she intends to use the product herself? If so, do you politely point out that the product contains lanolin and ask if she still wants to buy it?
   b) Keep quiet, it's up to her what she buys and your sales figures are down?
   c) Sell her the product and hope she doesn't come crying to you if it brings her out in a nasty rash?

3. *Mrs N asks for advice on skin care products. Since she has mature skin the most suitable product is also the most expensive. She seems impressed with the product, however she doesn't look very well off. Do you:*
   a) Resist the temptation to guess about her personal circumstances and sell her the best product?
   b) Talk her into a less effective but cheaper product because you are sure she can't afford the first one?
   c) Make her tell you what she earns so that you can be sure she can afford the product before agreeing to sell it to her?

4. *Miss F chooses a lash-lengthening mascara containing microfilaments. From her record card, you see she wears contact lenses. The tiny filaments could lodge beneath the lens and cause irritation. Do you:*

a) Explain that her chosen product is not suitable for contact lens wearers and recommend another?

b) Say nothing and sell her the product? She's the best person to judge whether it suits her or not.

c) Sell it to her but make her promise never to rub her eyes while she's wearing it?

5. *Miss S, a bridal client, insists on wearing a blue-based pale pink lipstick for her wedding make-up. You know this will photograph and video badly. Do you:*

a) Try to persuade her to try a more suitable colour by explaining that photographic make-up is different from everyday make-up?

b) Agree with her choice so that you don't offend her?

c) Refuse to do her make-up at all unless she does exactly as you say?

6. *A client with fine, dark upper lip hair books a waxing appointment. Given that waxing can distort the hair follicle and change the angle of hair growth and may even encourage stronger growth in the upper lip area, would you:*

a) Advise your client to try a bleaching treatment first, to remove the pigment rather than the entire hair.

b) Perform the treatment she asks for. If the hair gets stronger and more noticeable, you can then sell her a course of electro-epilation treatment.

c) Suggest she have her jaw and chin waxed while she's there, since you can notice a few dark downy hairs there too.

## Answers

'a's – Well done, you put client care above sales.
'b's – Oh-oh, never put sales above client care.
'c's – Agghhh! The therapist from hell strikes again!

# Chapter Fourteen

# *Something Extra*

*Become a chameleon. Adapt to meet individual clients' needs.*

## *Meet your client's needs*

Most women can paint their own nails and apply face creams. So, what brings your client to your salon? Your salon must offer something your client can't do for herself at home. Identify what that 'extra' something is in each treatment and make sure your client always gets it.

If the extra is missing, you won't get new clients and you'll begin to lose existing ones to more professional salons. Here are some reasons why your client may book a facial:

- to improve skin texture
- to have **comedones** or **milia** removed
- to have eyebrows tidied
- to have an hour of undisturbed relaxation
- to be pampered
- to relieve muscular tension in her face
- for an expert skin evaluation
- for expert skin care advice.

It's not enough to slop cream on and off your client while she has a nice lie-down. Technically, a facial has been performed but your client won't return. For her to become a regular client, you must *make a difference*. Even better, make your treatment so effective that she cannot do without it.

## *Offer specific improvement*

During **consultation**, isolate one or more specific areas to work on during treatment. During massage **consultation**, for example, find out what your client does. Keyboard workers love hand and arm massage; clients who do a lot of standing or walking benefit greatly from foot and leg massage; clients who bend and pick up small children particularly enjoy back massage. If your client has facial fluid retention, perform a lymphatic drainage massage in place of a regular relaxing facial massage.

## Pamper your client

Once you have made your client feel comfortable and cared for, think how you can make her feel pampered. The more thoughtful you are, the more valued your client will feel.

- Don't say, 'Next foot, please.' Lift her foot from the foot spa during pedicure.
- Place her hand into the bowl during manicure.
- Help her into and out of the steam bath.
- Help her on with her coat.
- Pass her handbag.
- Pass her sunbed goggles.

Yes, even offer to apply **UV** tanning cream to that hard-to-reach area on her back!

## Be flexible

Make your appointment times flexible to fit client need. What can you offer workers during their lunch-breaks? A 45-minute treatment. On Fridays and Saturdays, offer on-the-spot manicures by junior members of staff.

Make treatment itself flexible. For example, if your bridal client feels too 'made-up' in foundation, use a tinted moisturiser as a base for the colour cosmetics.

## Customize treatment

Beauty therapy is a personal service. How can you make *your* treatment even more special? Here are some suggestions. No doubt, you will think up your own ideas.

- Make clients feel cosy on chilly days by placing an electric blanket below the couch blanket.
- Tape relaxing music to be played through headphones to complement different parts of your facial or body treatment routine. (If you don't have a **performance licence**, you may only play music not subject to performance rights.)
- Offer a relaxing head massage during a face mask treatment.
- During the summer, offer an application of self-tanning lotion in place of moisturizer at the end of your client's facial.
- Offer a **complementary** jewellery cleaning service during manicure – but do remember to return your client's valuables at the end of treatment.

## Invite suggestions

Many large stores have a 'Comments box'. This may not be appropriate for a one-room salon but you get the idea. Rather than rely on clients to point out if your service or products fall short of their expectations, why not invite comments from clients and staff? Sometimes a message such as 'If you're pleased with our service, tell your friends. If you're not, tell us' appears on such boxes.

**Figure 14.1**
Ensure all client
information signs
are clear

You probably won't want to make every suggested change but even if you don't learn anything useful, inviting suggestions will show how much you value your clients' opinions.

## Make treatment effective

### Choose products and equipment wisely

For your clients to get the maximum benefit from treatment, your equipment and products must be as effective as possible. The beauty industry is continually marketing new and revamped products and equipment. Professional equipment is expensive. Don't be bamboozled into buying by company reps. Be sure to do your research to find out if products, treatments and equipment are based on scientific fact.

If you need advice on whether a product or equipment will be effective, contact a professional organization such as the British Association of Electrolysists or phone the **BABTAC** professional helpline, if you are a member. Think carefully about what your clients want before investing in new products or equipment.

- Consider the cost-effectiveness of product ranges. What percentage of profit is made on retail sales? Does the range include salon-size products which cut down on salon overheads?

- Can you use a couch-cum-chair rather than buy both pieces of equipment?

- Electrotherapy machines are prestigious but very expensive. Work out how many treatments you will need to give before making a profit.

- Most clients prioritize face above body. Expensive body therapy machines may take a long time to pay for themselves.

- Know what you are buying. Certain technological and pharmaceutical developments are patented and are not available in similar-looking products or machines.

- When considering tweezer methods of **electro-epilation** bear in mind that it's generally thought that the hair shaft above the skin lacks sufficient moisture to make it a good conductor of electricity.

> **Remember:** Never buy a product range or equipment on impulse simply because you like the look of it.

**Figure 14.2**
Research the market before investing in electrical equipment

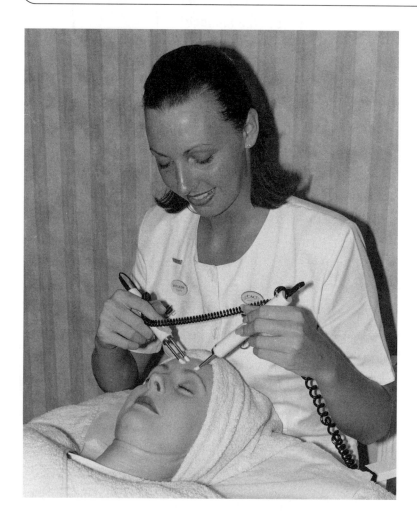

## *Give a full treatment*

Clients will only pay for a service that is good value. This doesn't mean that treatment must be cheap; it means the results of treatment must be worth the cost.

### *Facial treatment*

- Include the **décollete** area in a full facial.
- Tweeze stray eyebrow hairs.
- Remove **sebum** from blocked facial pores, remove **comedones** and **milia**.
- Include brief massage treatment to the **trapezius**, **deltoid** and top of the **biceps** and the top of the **pectoral** muscles.

## Body treatment

- Your client's course of slimming treatment will be far more successful combined with diet and exercise – monitor weight and body measurements and give plenty of encouragement.
- Pleasing aromas enhance massage. Tell your client which oils you are using during aromatherapy massage and explain their benefits. If you don't have aromatherapy qualifications, massage with ready-mixed aromatherapy oils.
- During back massage, include the **trapezius**, **deltoid** and **biceps**.

## Waxing

- Include the knee in a half-leg wax.
- Offer to wax hair from the big toe if it's noticeable.
- Offer to wax terminal hair from above as well as to the sides of the bikini-line.
- Offer to wax terminal hairs on the back of the upper thigh during bikini-line wax.

## Manicure and pedicure

- Lift and push back cuticles. Clients often have manicures to combat **pterygium**. Trim if necessary but don't over-trim.
- During massage, include the forearm or lower leg.
- If your manicure client doesn't want nail polish, finish by buffing and using a nail whitening pencil.
- Gently remove calluses from fingers, the heel and the ball of the foot with a pumice stone.
- Remove nicotine or ink stains with 20 per cent hydrogen peroxide.
- Gently clean under toenails with a cotton wool-tipped orangewood stick.

# Keep up with the beauty world

Women are interested in beauty. Today's newspapers and magazines are full of the latest fashions and trends. Your client will ask you about cosmetic trends, products and treatments that she's read about. Make sure you are at least as well informed as her by reading a professional salon magazine and keeping an eye on the beauty pages in the press.

Studying current trends can also help salon services. For example, current concern over sunbathing may mean professional self-tanning treatment may be a good treatment to promote.

## Give best advice

Use your in-depth knowledge of treatments and products and your professional judgement to give clients best advice. Information quickly becomes out of date, so be sure your information is accurate.

If current opinion is divided on a subject it's okay to say so. For example, some sources claim friction, shaving or plucking stimulates hair growth and some claim it doesn't. (Generally, shaving has been found not to stimulate hair growth and plucking has. The exception is eyebrow hair, which often gives up after one or two epilations.)

*Hints and tips*

Professional tips and hints will make your client feel special. Every month, research a few new ones. Your clients will love to hear practical advice and professional hints and tips from an 'insider' in the beauty business – it doesn't matter if you tell all your clients the same tip that week. For example, explain how a manicure can last several days longer if a top coat of clear polish is applied two or three days after polishing – you can even provide the top-coat. Offering health and hygiene advice also shows that you care about your client's well-being. For example, advise ear-piercing clients to wash then soak all newly bought earrings in surgical spirit before wearing them for the first time.

## *Keep learning*

Once you have qualified, continue to develop and refine your techniques to give the best results. Develop a facial and body massage routine that you enjoy. Add movements you learn from colleagues – experiment a little – there is art as well as science in good beauty therapy.

## Troubleshooting: Questions and Answers

### *Solutions to common technical problems*

1. **Q** *As you remove facial bleach from your client's upper lip, you notice whitened areas of skin. You also notice this on your own fingers. Have you accidentally bleached out skin colour?*

   **A** No. Normal reaction. Skin whitening can happen when hydrogen peroxide comes into contact with skin but should not be applied to broken skin. It is a harmless and temporary reaction. If it happens during treatment, explain this to your client before she sees it.

2. **Q** *You perform a full leg wax on a client who returns the following day to complain that, while her upper legs feel smooth, her lower legs feel bristly. Are you to blame?*

   **A** No. Normal reaction. It is unlikely to be poor waxing technique on the lower leg only. The more likely answer is that the hair growth on the client's upper legs was virgin growth while her lower leg hair had been recently shaved, disrupting the growth cycle. Some very short stubble on recently shaved legs cannot be prevented. Before waxing recently shaved legs, always warn your client that fine stubble, too short to wax, may appear during the following week. You can sometimes feel this stubble before applying the wax.

3. **Q** *You apply a thin layer of wax to your client's leg, it's a very cold day and you notice her skin is chilled. When you rip off the strip, the wax doesn't stick to the strip but stays on your client's leg. Your client complains of discomfort. The wax appears hard and pale. Is your technique at fault?*

   **A** No. Normal reaction. Very cold weather can cool the wax too quickly. To remedy this, rub your hand firmly and quickly over the strip several times to warm the wax through friction. The wax should then come off in the usual way. This problem can be prevented by:
   - heating the treatment room sufficiently during cold weather
   - ensuring a chilly client is warmed through before waxing
   - using a wax especially formulated for cold weather.

**Troubleshooting continued**

4. **Q** *You apply a thin layer of wax to your client's leg, it's a very hot day and you notice her skin is very warm. When you rip off the strip, it doesn't come away cleanly. It looks gluey and feels very sticky. Your client complains of discomfort. Is your technique at fault?*

   **A** No. Normal reaction. Very warm weather can stop wax cooling sufficiently. This problem can be prevented by:

   - cooling the treatment room sufficiently during hot weather
   - ensuring an overheated client cools down before waxing
   - using a wax especially formulated for hot weather.

5. **Q** *During an under-arm wax, your client's hair follicles leak a small amount of blood, which alarms her. This sometimes happens when you wax bikini-lines. Is your technique at fault?*

   **A** No. Normal reaction. It is normal for the follicles of very strongly rooted **terminal** hair to leak a little blood. Immediately cover the area with a cooling pad of witch hazel, reassure your client (if she noticed) and be sure to explain waxing aftercare. Dispose of the witch hazel pad in a lined, lidded bin.

6. **Q** *Your client develops a bruise during a bikini-line wax. This sometimes happens when you wax under arms. Is this simply an allergic reaction to the wax or the treatment?*

   **A** No. The release of **histamine** causing *mild* **erythema** and **oedema** is a normal reaction to hair removal. An allergic reaction to depilatory wax would appear as *severe* and **prolonged erythema** and **oedema**. Under-arm and bikini-line skin is thin with a good blood supply which makes it very prone to bruising. This is always the result of bad practice and a common mistake.

7. **Q** *During an eyebrow wax, you remove the strip to discover that most of the client's eyebrow has been waxed off! Is your technique at fault?*

   **A** Yes. This happens when too much wax is applied below the eyebrow. The waxing strip presses the wax further into the eyebrow and too many brow hairs are pulled off. If this happens, match up the other brow and explain that you've trimmed the brow a little too thinly. Apologize and don't charge.

   To prevent this happening, apply the wax as thinly as possible using an orange wood stick, paying particular attention to the area directly below the eyebrow. Press on the waxing strip carefully to avoid pushing wax into the body of the brow.

8. **Q** *After completing a course of electo-epilation, you notice your client's upper lip has developed a wrinkled appearance. Is your electro-epilation technique at fault?*

   **A** Bad practice. Over-treating hairs in close proximity can dehydrate the underlying tissues and encourage premature wrinkling.

9. **Q** *During electro-epilation to the eyebrow area, a bruise results as you insert the correct size of probe. Is your electro-epilation technique at fault?*

   **A** Not necessarily. The thin skin and good blood supply in this area make it very prone to bruising; even the finest electrolysis probe can catch a blood vessel. Bruising cannot always be prevented. Before performing electrolysis to the eyebrows, always warn your client that this can result in a bruise looking similar to a black eye and explain the reasons.

**Troubleshooting continued**

If you bruise other areas during **electro-epilation** this could be due to bad practice. Your probe may be too thick for the hair follicle. (You can gauge the size of the follicle by the width of its hair.) Or you may be inserting the probe inaccurately.

**10. Q** *Your client returns several months after you pierced her ears. She complains of lumpy overgrowth on the site of the pierce on both ears. Did you perform the pierce badly?*

**A** No, but you failed to check that your client wasn't prone to keloid scarring. This is when injury to the skin 'over-heals', with excessive tissue repair, creating a raised scar. Black skins are especially prone to keloid scarring. Before piercing or performing **electro-epilation** on black clients in particular, ask if they have any raised scarring.

# PART THREE

# Useful Information

# *Regulations Under the Health and Safety at Work Act 1974*

| Health and Safety Regulations | Coverage |
|---|---|
| Workplace (Health, Safety and Welfare) Regulations 1992 | Cover a wide range of basic health, safety and welfare issues. |
| Management of Health and Safety at Work Regulations 1992 | Require employers to carry out risk assessments, implement necessary measures, appoint competent people and arrange for appropriate information and training. |
| Control of Substances Hazardous to Health Regulations 1994 (COSHH) | Require employers to assess the risks from handling hazardous substances and take appropriate precautions. |
| Chemicals (Hazard Information and Packing for Supply) Regulations 1994 | Require suppliers to classify, label and package dangerous chemicals and provide safety data sheets for them. |
| Reporting of Injuries, Diseases and Dangerous Occurrences Regulations 1995 (RIDDOR) | Require employers to notify certain occupational injuries and dangerous events. |
| Manual Handling Regulations 1992 | Require loads to be handled safely. |
| Personal Protective Equipment Regulations 1992 (PPE) | Require employers to provide appropriate protective equipment or clothing for employees. |
| Health and Safety (First Aid) Regulations 1981 | Cover requirements for first aid. |
| Health and Safety (Display Screen Equipment) Regulations 1992 | Set out requirements for work with visual display units (VDUs) |
| Provision and Use of Work Equipment Regulations 1992 (PUWER) | Require that equipment and machinery provided for use at work are safe. |
| Electricity at Work Regulations 1989 | Require employees using electrical equipment to ensure that it is safe to use and maintained in a safe condition. |
| Gas Safety (Installation and Use) Regulations 1994 | Cover the safe installation, maintenance and use of gas appliances. |

# Useful Addresses

## Training bodies

City & Guilds of London Institute
1 Giltspur Street
London EC1A 9DD
Tel: 020 7294 2468
Fax: 020 7294 2400/5
http.//www.city-and-guilds.co.uk

International Therapy Examination Council
(ITEC)
James House, 10/11 Heathfield Terrace
Chiswick
London W4 JE
Tel: 020 8994 4141
Fax: 020 8994 7880
E-mail info@itecworld.co.uk

## General trade associations

The British Association of Beauty Therapy
and Cosmetology (BABTAC)
Parabola House
Parabola Road
Cheltenham
Gloucestershire GL50 3AH
Tel: 01242 570284

The Beauty Industry Authority (BIA)
2nd Floor, Fraser House
Nether Hall Road
Doncaster
South Yorkshire DN1 2PH
Tel: 01302 380020

Fax: 01302 380028
http.//www.bia.org.uk

Guild of Professional Beauty Therapists
PO Box 310
Derby DE23 9BR
Tel: 01332 771714
Fax: 01332 771742
E-mail lynne@beauty-guild.co.uk

Independent Professional Therapists,
International (IPTI)
St Michael's Place
58a Bridgegate
Retford
Notts DN22 7UZ
Tel: 01777 700383
Fax: 01777 708741

International Aestheticiennes (IA)
Bache Hall
Bache Hall Estate
Chester
Cheshire CH2 1BR
Tel: 01244 376539
Fax: 01244 373571

## Specialized trade associations

British Association of Electrolysis Ltd (BAE)
2a Tudor Way
Hillingdon
Uxbridge UB10 9AB
Tel: 01895 239966

Institute of Electrolysis Ltd
138 Downs Barn Boulevard
Downs Barn
Milton Keynes MK14 7RP
Tel/Fax: 01908 695297

The British Micropigmentation Society
118 Baker Street
London W1M 1LB
Tel: 020 7486 6291

The Aromatherapy Organisations Council
3 Latymer Close
Baybrook
Market Harborough
Leicester LE16 8LN
Tel: 01858 465731

The International Nail Association (INA)
2nd Floor, Fraser House
Nether Hall Road
Doncaster
South Yorkshire DN1 2PH
Tel: 01302 380000
Fax: 01302 380028
E-mail ina@habia.org

The Sunbed Association
Rapier House
40–46 Lamb's Conduit Street
London WC1N 3NW
Tel: 020 7405 0682
Fax: 020 7405 6609

British Association of Skin Camouflage
(BASC)
South Park Road
Macclesfield
Stockport
Cheshire SK11 6SH
Tel: 01652 267880

Fax: 01652 267879
E-mail basc@resources.demon.co.uk

(BISA) British International Spa Association
Spa House
Winchet Hall
Goudhurst
Kent TN17 1JY
Tel: 01580 211055
Fax: 01580 212062

## Government bodies

Her Majesty's Stationery Office (HMSO)
Publications Centre
PO Box 276
London SW8 5DT
http://www.hmso.gov.uk

The Data Protection Registrar
Wycliffe House
Water Lane
Wilmslow
Cheshire SK9 5AF
Tel: 01625 545745
http://www.open.gov.uk\dpr\dprhome.htm

Health and Safety Executive (HSE)
Information Centre
Broad Lane
Sheffield S3 7HQ
InfoLine: 0541 545500
http://www.open.gov.uk/hse/hsehome.htm

Employment Medical Advisory Service
Health and Safety Executive
14 Cardiff Road
Luton
Beds LU1 1PP
Tel: 01582 444226

# Glossary

| | |
|---|---|
| **aesthetician/aestheticienne** | (*pronounced ace-thet-ishon*) an alternative term for beautician or beatuy therapist |
| **agnail** | a hang nail |
| **ambient temperature** | the surrounding temperature |
| **amenorrhoea** | abnormal absence of menstruation |
| **anomaly** | irregularity |
| **assertiveness** | firmly and calmly stating one's position |
| **automatic tweezers** | spring-loaded tweezers |
| | |
| **BABTAC** | British Association of Beauty Therapy and Cosmetology |
| **beautician** | a therapist qualified to treat mainly the face, hands and feet |
| **beauty consultant** | a consultant trained to advise on branded make-up and skin care products |
| **beauty therapist** | a therapist qualified to treat the whole body, including the use of electrical treatments such as electro-epilation |
| **best practice** | the working methods industry considers most desirable |
| **biceps** | the two-headed muscle which bends the elbow |
| **body language** | communication through conscious or unconscious physical gestures and poses |
| **by-law** | a regulation enforced by the local authority |
| | |
| **CAB** | Citizens' Advice Bureau |
| **cancellation fee** | a fee charged in compensation for a last-minute appointment cancellation or a missed appointment |
| **carcinogenic** | causing cancer |
| **cataract** | thickening of the eye lens |
| **chloasma** | patches of brown pigmentation due to a localized increase of melanin |
| **clientele** | group of clients |
| **code of conduct** | an agreed industry standard of good practice |
| **comedo/comedone** | blackhead |
| **complementary treatment** | a treatment given free of charge |
| **consultation card** | a card used for noting down salon clients' personal details (also called a **record card**) |
| **consultation** | an appointment to discuss treatment |

| | |
|---|---|
| **consumable goods** | goods and products used up during treatment (also called **consumables**) |
| **contact dermatitis** | a scaly skin condition, similar to eczema |
| **contagious** | (referring to a disease) passed on by physical contact |
| **contra-indicated** | when using a substance or treatment could be harmful to a client with a particular condition |
| **contra-indication** | a factor in a client's condition which indicates *against* the use of a particular substance or treatment |
| **corrugator supercilii** | the muscle lying beneath the eyebrow |
| **cosmetologist** | an alternative name for a beautician |
| **council** | a term for the local authority |
| **cross-infection** | when one person contaminates an object which then infects a second person |
| **décollete** | the area of the neck and chest above the breasts |
| **deltoid** | the triangular muscle which covers the shoulder joint and raises the arm away from the body |
| **deportment** | physical bearing and carriage |
| **dietician** | a person qualified to advise on diet, exercise and body shape |
| **disposable income** | spare income after tax and payment of essential bills |
| **effleurage** | a stroking movement made with the palm of the hand in massage |
| **electro-epilation** | electrical treatment to remove superfluous hair (also called **electrolysis**) |
| **electrologist** | a person qualified in electro-epilation |
| **electrolysis** | electro-epilation |
| **empathy** | the ability to identify oneself mentally with others |
| **endocrine** | hormone secreted directly into the bloodstream from ductless glands |
| **epilation** | hair removal. In beauty therapy, epilation generally refers to hair removal by electro-epilation |
| **erythema** | flushing of the skin caused by dilated blood capillaries |
| **ethics** | moral principles and rules of conduct |
| **EU** | European Union |
| **exfoliation** | removal of the top layer of skin scales |
| **feedback** | response |
| **FIFO** | a stock rotation mnemonic 'First In, First Out' |
| **galvanism** | a stimulating electrical treatment |
| **Health and Safety Inspector** | a local authority inspector concerned with health and hygiene |
| **high-frequency treatment** | a stimulating electrical treatment |
| **hirsutism** | excessive 'abnormal' (in women) hair growth |
| **hirsute** | suffering from **hirsutism** |
| **histamine** | a substance produced by the body which causes blood vessels to dilate |
| **HMSO** | Her Majesty's Stationery Office |
| **hypertrichosis** | excessive hair growth in 'normal' areas |
| **indicated** | when treatment is thought to be beneficial |
| **intercom** | a system of intercommunication between rooms |
| **IR** | infra red |
| **irritant** | a substance which causes irritation to skin tissues |
| **lanugo hair** | fine downy hair found on newborn babies |

| | |
|---|---|
| **legislation** | laws |
| **liaise** | to act as a link |
| **limescale** | calcium carbonate deposit |
| **local authority** | a group of representatives elected by local people, responsible for drawing up and enforcing local by-laws |
| **masseter** | the main chewing muscle |
| **melanocytes** | cells producing pigment |
| **menopause** | the ceasing of monthly periods |
| **menopausal** | going through the menopause |
| **menstruation** | a monthly period |
| **micropigmentation** | pigment applied to the top layer of the skin using a fine needle (also called semi-permanent make-up) |
| **milium** | (plural milia) a hard, round 'pearl' of keratin trapped below the epidermis |
| **minor** | anyone under 18 |
| **misconduct** | unprofessional behaviour |
| **misinformation** | misleading information |
| **National Insurance** | compulsory payments made by employees to fund state benefit |
| **obese** | excessively fat |
| **oedema** | accumulation of fluid in body tissue, characterized by swelling |
| **oxidation** | the process of combining or causing to combine with oxygen |
| **pacemaker** | a device fitted internally to regulate heartbeat |
| **paronychia** | inflammation of the skin surrounding the nail |
| **patch test** | a skin test made *before* treatment to determine whether the client is sensitive to a product |
| **pathogen** | an agent which causes disease |
| **pectoral** | relating to the chest |
| **performance licence** | a licence permitting public performance of licensed musicians' work |
| **pétrissage** | a compression movement used in massage |
| **plasma** | the watery fluid in which blood cells and other blood constituents are suspended |
| **platysma** | a sheet of muscle under the skin of the neck |
| **pterygium/pterygium unguium** | (the 'p' is not pronounced) overgrowth of the cuticle which becomes attached to the nail plate |
| **rapport** | a harmonious relationship |
| **record card** | a card used for noting down salon clients' personal details (also called a **consultation card**) |
| **red vein cauterization** | an electrical treatment which seals broken thread veins |
| **rep** | 'representative' generally employed by a sales company |
| **seborrhoea** | a skin condition characterized by excess **sebum** production |
| **sebum** | oil secreted by the sebaceous glands of the skin |
| **sensitizer** | a substance which creates an abnormal sensitivity |
| **service industry** | an industry which provides the public with a service rather than goods |
| **shelf-life** | the length of time for which a stored product remains usable |
| **solvent** | a substance able to dissolve another substance to form a solution |

| | |
|---|---|
| **sternum** | the breastbone |
| **stock rotation** | the practice of shelving stock so that the oldest stock is purchased first |
| **superfluous hair** | normal but unwanted hair growth |
| **tapotement** | stimulating massage movements also known as percussion, e.g. hacking and clapping |
| **terminal hair** | coarse, dark hair found on the scalp, under-arm and bikini-line regions |
| **tinea** | a fungal infection also known as athlete's foot and ringworm |
| **toluenediamine** | a tint used in lash and brow tinting |
| **toxic** | poisonous |
| **trachea** | the windpipe |
| **trapezius** | a muscle of the neck, shoulder and back |
| **true steam** | vapour from boiling water not yet mixed with air, e.g. from the mouth of a steamer or kettle |
| **umbilicus** | the navel |
| **use-by date** | the date by which a product must be used |
| **UV** | ultra violet |
| **vacuum suction** | an electrical treatment to stimulate lymphatic drainage |
| **VAT** | Value Added Tax |
| **vellus hair** | soft, fine hair which covers the body |
| **verruca** | (plural verrucae) a wart, especially one growing on the base of the foot |
| **virgin hair** | (in beauty therapy) previously untreated hair |
| **volatile** | quick to evaporate |
| **walk-in** | a client who enters the salon with no appointment to enquire about services or goods |

# Bibliography

- Almond, E. (1998) *Safety in the Salon. A Guide for Hairdressing and Beauty Professionals*, Macmillan, Basingstoke.
- Bennett, R. (1995) *The Science of Beauty Therapy*, 2nd edition, Hodder & Stoughton, London.
- Cartwright, E., Morris, G., Sullivan, M. (1995) *Electro-epilation: A Practical Approach for NVQ Level 3*, Stanley Thornes Ltd, Cheltenham.
- Eaton, A., Openshaw, F. (1988) *Cosmetic Make-up and Manicure*, Longman, Harlow.
- Hinkel, A., Lind, R. (1983) *Electrolysis, Thermolysis and the Blend: The Principles and Practice of Permanent Hair Removal*, Arroway, California.
- Howard, G. (1987) *The Principles and Practice of Perfumery and Cosmetics*, Stanley Thornes Ltd, Cheltenham.
- McGuinness, H. (1997) *Aromatherapy Beauty Therapy Basics*, Hodder & Stoughton, London.
- Nicholson, M. (1996) *Office Practice: Business Administration for NVQ, City and Guilds and BTEC*, Macmillan, Basingstoke.
- Nordmann, L. (1995) *Beauty Therapy – The Foundations NVQ/SVQ 1&2*, Macmillan, Basingstoke.
- Rounce, J. (1983) *Science for the Beauty Therapist*, Stanley Thornes Ltd, Cheltenham.
- Simmons, J.V. (1995) *Science and The Beauty Business*, Macmillan, Basingstoke.
- Simms, J. (1993) *A Practical Guide to Beauty Therapy for NVQ Level 2*. Stanley Thornes Ltd, Cheltenham.
- Smith, T. (ed.) (1993) *The British Medical Association Complete Family Health Encyclopaedia*, Dorling Kindersley, London.
- Winyard, G. (1992) *A Guide for Health and Beauty Therapists, Volume 2: The Body*. Longman, Harlow.
- Winyard, G. (1996) *A Guide for Health and Beauty Therapists, Volume 1: Face, Hands and Feet*, 2nd edition, Longman, Harlow.

# Index

Page numbers for figures, tables etc. are given in italics.